Waste Not, Want Not in Applewell

Lilac Mills lives on a Welsh mountain with her very patient husband and incredibly sweet dog, where she grows veggies (if the slugs don't get them), bakes (badly) and loves making things out of glitter and glue (a mess, usually). She's been an avid reader ever since she got her hands on a copy of *Noddy Goes to Toytown* when she was five, and she once tried to read everything in her local library starting with A and working her way through the alphabet. She loves long, hot summer days and cold winter ones snuggled in front of the fire, but whatever the weather she's usually writing or thinking about writing, with heartwarming romance and happy-ever-afters always on her mind.

Also by Lilac Mills

A Very Lucky Christmas
Sunshine at Cherry Tree Farm
Summer on the Turquoise Coast
Love in the City by the Sea

Tanglewood Village series

The Tanglewood Tea Shop
The Tanglewood Flower Shop
The Tanglewood Wedding Shop

Island Romance

Sunrise on the Coast
Holiday in the Hills
Sunset on the Square

Applewell Village

Waste Not, Want Not in Applewell

LILAC MILLS

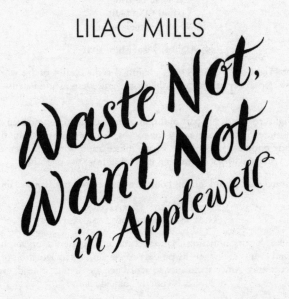

Waste Not, Want Not in Applewell

ᴍCANELO

First published in the United Kingdom in 2021 by

Canelo
31 Helen Road
Oxford OX2 0DF
United Kingdom

A CIP catalogue record for this book is available from the British Library.

Print ISBN 978 1 80032 316 2
Ebook ISBN 978 1 80032 315 5

Look for more great books at www.canelo.co

Printed and bound in Great Britain by Clays Ltd, Elcograf S.p.A.

To Dad, whose garage shelves were always stacked with jars of nails, screws, washers, all of them neatly labelled and most of them rusty...

Chapter 1

George

'Looking dapper as usual, George,' a voice called out, and George Nightingale tipped an imaginary hat in the speaker's direction, then bent down to pick up a newspaper from the stand near the door. He didn't want to get into a conversation with Donald Mousel. He never wanted to get into a conversation with anyone.

'Just the paper?' Sid, the fellow who owned the newsagent, asked.

'Yes, please.' Sid asked him the same question every morning and received the same answer. It was practically a ritual, and George wasn't sure whether the Earth might stop turning if either of them deviated from it.

George paid for his paper, counting the coins out carefully, and tried not to read the headlines as he did so. Getting sucked into the story on the front page wasn't part of the plan.

'Straight back home, is it?' Donald asked.

'Of course.'

'Doing anything nice today?'

'I'll be working.'

'Not retired yet, then?'

George forced out a smile. 'Not yet.' At fifty-eight, he had another nine years to go before he could draw on his state pension.

'I remember them days,' Donald said. 'Used to get up at six every morning, regular as clockwork, then it was off to the daily grind.' He sounded wistful, as though he missed it. 'My, how things have changed.'

George wasn't sure whether the man was referring to his status as a retiree, or to George's ability to work from home.

'I still do a spot of taxi work now and again, just to keep my hand in when they're running short.' Donald nodded to himself and sighed. 'Looks like it's a nice day for it,' he continued.

'A nice day for what?' George asked. Was there something going on in Applewell he didn't know about? The village fête wasn't scheduled until later in the year, May Day had come and gone, and the next bank holiday was a couple of weeks away. All of those things were high points in the village's calendar, but none of them were imminent.

Donald frowned. 'Today, it looks like a nice day for today,' he clarified, leaving George none the wiser.

'Oh, good,' George said. Every morning he washed the shirt and underwear he'd worn yesterday and hung them out to dry, or draped it over the radiator next to his desk if the weather was inclement. A shadow flitted across his mind as he thought about radiators, but he pushed it away. With any luck, the spell of dry weather would hold for a while and he wouldn't have to think just yet about the clanking coming from the ancient boiler when he turned the heating on.

Therefore, he didn't.

He was good at that. Compartmentalising things was a speciality of his. Everything in its place, and a place for everything was a mantra he lived by, and why should the contents of his mind be any different to that of his house?

He picked up his paper and turned to leave, but Donald was standing immediately behind him. The aisle was too narrow for him to squeeze past, so he stepped to the side and attempted to leave the shop via the confectionary aisle, but Mrs Hayworth was blocking it with her pull-along trolley thing.

'All right, George?' was her chirpy greeting to him. 'Wanna get past?'

'If you don't mind,' he replied, anticipating she would either go to the end of the aisle or she could squash herself up against the pick-n-mix.

She did neither. She didn't move an inch.

'Next door has been sold, I see,' she said.

'Pardon?'

'I *said*, the house next door to yours has been sold.'

George frowned. 'Has it?' The 'For Sale' sign had still been in its customary position this morning. 'Are you sure?'

'Definitely.'

'Who has bought it?' It had been empty for months, ever since old Alys Griffiths had died.

Mrs Hayworth took a step closer to him and leant in, her voice a conspiratorial whisper. 'Her name is Nessa Millbrook and she's from England.' The latter word was spoken with some degree of suspicion mixed with annoyance.

George suppressed a snort. Folks around these parts weren't too keen on people from away buying up properties as second homes then hardly ever living in them, and normally he'd agree with the general consensus that second-homers were bad for the community. But in this instance, he was pleased the house next door to him would only be used occasionally. He wasn't keen on neighbours, and his fellow villagers were far too nosey for his liking. The second-homers were notorious for keeping themselves to themselves and not integrating. Which suited him perfectly.

'And did you know Maisie Beddoes is pregnant *again*, and John Porter lost a cow last night?' Mrs Hayworth continued. 'I bumped into his wife this morning on the way to pick up her prescription from the chemist and she was telling me all about it.'

'No, I didn't. How did it happen?' George wasn't at all interested, but he prided himself on being courteous, despite his reluctance to interact with his fellow villagers.

Mrs Hayworth shrugged. 'Don't ask me, I don't know nothing about cows.'

Neither did George. He might have grown up in Applewell and had lived there since moving back from the bright lights of Liverpool in order to look after his father when his mother died, but cows weren't his speciality, despite the village sitting slap bang in rural West Wales.

'If you see her, send her my regards,' George said, politely.

'You'll probably see her before I will, so you can send them yourself.'

'Will I?' George was perplexed. He didn't bump into Angharad Porter very often, despite her living in the farm at the end of his lane.

'She's moving in today.'

'Moving where?'

Mrs Hayworth let out a sigh. 'It's right what they say about you,' she muttered, just loud enough for him to hear, then she spoke in a more normal tone. 'The house next door to you.'

'Angharad Porter?'

4

'Why would *she* be moving—? Heaven help us: not *her*, your new neighbour! *Nessa Millbrook.*'

'Ah, I see. Apologies. Crossed wires. Must be off. Work, you know.' Despite his reluctance to touch the woman, George squeezed past, anxious to leave. What had she meant by that comment about him? What were people saying about him?

He wished the good people of Applewell would mind their own business. That was the last time he'd exchange pleasantries with Mrs Hayworth, although he could honestly say nothing about his encounter with her had been pleasant.

Crossly, George marched along the pavement towards Pins to Elephants, lamenting on the unavoidable issues of living in a small community, and a frisson of unease travelled down his chest to coil in his belly.

He'd have to be extra vigilant, that was all, he told himself. He was careful to ensure the bungalow was neat and tidy outside, while nets up at every window ensured his privacy.

Now, what did he want in here, he wondered, as he came to a halt in the shop's doorway. Oh, yes, a new radio. For some inexplicable reason, his had abruptly stopped working yesterday evening. He'd fiddled with it, tapped it, unplugged it and plugged it back in, then banged it hard with the flat of his hand, before finally acknowledging it was defunct.

With great reluctance, he concluded he needed to purchase a new one because he liked listening to Radio 4 whilst he was working and simply couldn't be without one. He'd not throw the old one out though, because it might come in handy for parts.

'Excuse me.'

George glanced around to see an unfamiliar woman standing far too close to him, and he realised he was blocking the door to Pins to Elephants. She was smiling at him and he was tempted to smile back but he resisted, wondering where the unaccustomed and unwarranted urge to be friendly had come from.

'Apologies,' he said, moving to one side to let her pass, guessing her to be a tourist. The village and surrounding areas abounded with them, especially at this time of year. Although, most of them weren't quite as keen to visit Applewell in winter when storms howled in off the Irish Sea and the temperature felt low enough to rival the North Pole.

'Thanks,' was the woman's response and he followed her inside, his gaze sweeping over her as he headed for the relevant section of the shop. She was possibly somewhere in her early fifties. Her hair was a palette of brown, grey and silver, and she wore it to her shoulders where it curled and bounced whenever she turned her head. Crow's feet creased the corners of her eyes and she continued to smile as she wandered around the shop.

There was something about her that drew him, and he hastily looked away, anxious not to be caught staring. What on earth was the matter with him today? he asked himself. It wasn't like him to take an interest in anyone, especially someone of the opposite sex. Having to deviate from his usual routine of only visiting the newsagents on his morning walk must be getting to him.

While he waited to be served after finding the radio he wanted, he noticed the woman from earlier examining tins of cat food, and George forced his attention onto a display of camping equipment. When the shop boasted they sold anything and everything they were clearly exaggerating, but George was forced to admit they did have an impressive variety of items, such as gardening equipment, electrical goods, sewing stuff, pegs and so on. If he needed anything non-food related, this was his go-to place to... well... go to.

Purchase made, George accepted the paper bag in which his radio had been carefully placed, tucked the parcel under his arm, and tried not to make eye contact with the woman who was waiting her turn to be served.

He left the shop hurriedly and made his way back through the village to his bungalow, thankful there were few people on the road today and even fewer cars. One of his pet hates was to be beeped at and waved. There was no need for it, and he was grateful that the one car he saw ignored him.

His bungalow lay on a lane on the outskirts of the village, the last house on the track which led to John Porter's farm, so there was no through traffic and very few people went past except for John and his wife and other necessary farm personnel. The relative seclusion suited George very well indeed and, for a few years now, he'd been even more isolated due to the fact the old lady who'd lived in the cottage next door to him had died and the property had remained empty ever since.

Not now though, he saw, as he rounded the bend in the lane and spied a car in the neighbouring drive. It was the same one that had driven past him a few moments ago, and he guessed it must belong to his new neighbour.

How tiresome.

He hoped this Nessa Millbrook woman wouldn't prove to be a nuisance. He could do without noisy children, or loud music, or teenagers slouching around looking moody and littering the hedgerow with cigarette ends and cans of lager.

George hastened up his drive, opened his front door a crack and slipped inside, relief flooding through him.

His relief was short-lived, however, broken by the sound of a large vehicle trundling up the lane and rumbling to a halt on the road outside his house, instead of carrying on to the farm.

George, still clutching his newspaper and the new radio, wove his way through the hall and into the sitting room until he reached his desk which was positioned underneath the window. He placed both items down on it and weaselled himself into the space between an armchair and the Welsh dresser which was piled high with glass jars. Peeping through the net curtain, he saw that the vehicle he'd heard was a van belonging to a removal company. It said so in big letters emblazoned down the side.

Two men got out, one of them carrying a sheaf of papers. The man carrying the papers looked at the topmost one, then at the cottage. 'This is the right address,' George heard him say as he walked up the path to the front door.

George shook his head in irritation. All this coming and going wasn't on. His morning routine had already been severely disrupted, and now this!

All he hoped was that the removal men would soon be on their way, and life would return to normal. Because he simply couldn't cope with any further disturbance today.

Chapter 2

Nessa

Nessa Millbrook watched in satisfaction as her new home began to fill up with her belongings. Not that she'd brought a great deal with her, having taken the move to Applewell and the cute little cottage as an opportunity to have a good clear-out. In Nessa's opinion, there was nothing better than having a good sort through and declutter. But seeing her sofa positioned on the rug she'd recently bought to cover the flagstone floor, her TV on its stand in the corner and the bookcase which had once belonged to her mother in an alcove next to the chimney breast, the place already started to feel homelier.

'That can go into the first bedroom at the top of the stairs,' she told the removal men as they huffed into the hall, carrying a chest of drawers between them. Nessa bit back a smile; she was quite enjoying herself, feeling as though she was directing traffic.

While they staggered up the stairs, she fished the kettle out of the box marked 'kitchen', found some mugs, long-life milk, coffee, tea bags and sugar in the same box and proceeded to make them all a well-earned cuppa. Once she'd done that, she'd fetch Sylvia, her incredibly vocal Siamese cat, who was currently in her travelling basket in the back of the car and was probably desperate to get

9

out. Uncertain where in the myriad boxes she'd stashed the cat food, Nessa had popped into the first shop she'd come across as she had entered Applewell. It was rather aptly named Pins to Elephants, she'd realised when she'd seen the variety of things the store stocked. Poor Sylvia must be thinking she was being put on survivor rations – the cat would normally have had her breakfast by now, but she had yet to be fed as Nessa had been keen to get on the road and arrive at the cottage as early as possible this morning.

'There's tea in the kitchen, if you want it,' she told the men when they stomped back down the stairs. Leaving them to it, she went out to the car to free Sylvia from her padded prison.

Nessa grinned. She could hear the cat yowling from the front step, and the car was parked down at the edge of the drive (which, admittedly, wasn't very long) and partly on the overgrown lawn, to allow the van to pull up as near to the front door as possible. That cat was loud.

'Sylvia, Sylvia,' Nessa crooned. 'What's all the fuss about? You don't like being shut in, do you, my sweetie?'

The cat yowled even louder as Nessa unlocked the travel box and eased the protesting cat out. Once in her mistress' arms, Sylvia's cries immediately turned to purrs and she rubbed her cheek against Nessa's.

Nessa let her cuddle for a while, before attaching a thin red leather lead to the leather collar around the cat's neck and putting her down onto the grass.

Cats generally didn't get taken for walks, but this one did, although she had also been allowed outside on her own when they had lived in Nessa's old house in Bristol. It would be a while before Sylvia would be permitted to roam free here, however – the cat would have to get used to the house first, and then the garden, before Nessa felt confident enough to let her wander.

For now, Sylvia could remain on the lead, especially with the cottage's doors having to stay open because of the removal men; she couldn't risk her escaping into unfamiliar territory and getting lost.

Sylvia took one tentative, delicate step forward, her body low to the ground, her ears swivelling to catch the unfamiliar sounds and her nose twitching at the new smells. This cottage in a little village two miles from the coast of West Wales was a far cry from the busy urban streets of Bristol she was used to, and Nessa could only imagine the assault on the cat's senses as the feline tried to make sense of the new world she suddenly found herself in.

'You'll like it,' she promised. 'Lots of grass, and trees, and fields to explore. Mice and voles to catch, birds to chase...' Not that the cat caught much, thankfully. One present of a dead mouse had been enough and Nessa shuddered at the memory.

As she stood there for a moment to allow Sylvia to stretch her legs, Nessa gazed at the cottage in pleasure. From the outside it was picture-postcard cute, with the obligatory climbing rose growing up a trellis on the one side of the door, a grey slate roof and rough stone walls. It needed renovating inside, but only the kitchen and bathroom could do with a complete overhaul, the rest of it needing a lick of paint and some TLC. Nessa was good at TLC and she was looking forward to lavishing some on the cottage, although she wasn't as good at decorating and DIY was way out of her league. Apart from that, the house itself was quite sound and she had no intention of covering up the flagstone floors with fitted carpets or blocking up the original fireplaces. The upstairs floorboards needed sanding and varnishing, but considering it had been standing empty for so long, the building was in remarkably good condition.

She'd fallen in love with it the moment she'd seen it, which was a surprise considering it had been relatively early in the morning on a wet and grey March day. She'd arrived on the dot at nine a.m., and by ten past nine she'd informed the estate agent she intended to put in an offer.

And now here she was, some weeks later, the proud owner of her forever home. Not quite the cottage by the sea that she'd envisioned when she'd told the hospital she wanted to take early retirement, but the lower price reflected its lack of sea view and she didn't think she'd miss seeing the cool grey waters of the Irish Sea every morning when she had rolling hills and huge skies to stare at instead. Applewell itself was a mere two miles from the coast and in a little dip, but the lane her cottage was on sloped up from the village and the extra height made for the most wonderful views across the hills surrounding it.

Nessa felt she had the best of both worlds. Two miles to the sea was no distance at all – she could walk it easily and she fully intended to – plus she had lush fields and woodland just outside her front door.

A tiny movement caught her attention and her gaze slid from her own house to the one next door. The bungalow was slightly elevated compared to her own because of the lane's gradient, and she could see it clearly despite the low hedge separating the front gardens of the two properties. The gravel drive was weed-free, the bins were neatly lined up near the garage, and net curtains covered all the windows. It looked well kept, and she wondered who lived there.

Another small movement, which she was certain was a twitch of a net curtain, made her hastily look away. It was only natural the neighbours would be curious about her, but she didn't want their first impression to be her gawping at them over the privet.

Still, while she stood there, ostensibly watching Sylvia, she couldn't help taking little glances out of the corner of her eye.

The one and only time she had been here previously was when she had decided to buy the cottage, and apart from a cursory look to make sure the neighbouring properties appeared decent enough, she hadn't taken a great deal of notice of the houses on either side. Her little house was last but one in the lane, and the cottage to the right as she looked up her drive was similar to hers, as were nearly all of the others in the row of semi-detached, two-up two-down, stone-built, slate-roofed affairs which appeared to be of a similar age to her own. The house which her own had several pots filled with flowers around the front door.

However, the bungalow to the left of Nessa's house was probably a hundred years younger, had a red-tiled roof and rendered walls which had been painted white. She wondered what the bungalow looked like inside. Was the net-curtain twitcher looking through a bedroom or a living-room window? How many people lived there? Were there any children?

She couldn't see evidence of any children in either of her immediate neighbours' gardens, such as a bike on the lawn or a basketball hoop attached a wall, but that was no real indication. She wondered what the twitcher in the bungalow was making of her, especially since she was standing on her front lawn with a cat attached to the end of a red leather lead. She hoped they didn't think she was a typical middle-aged cat lady. Nessa conceded she most definitely looked middle-aged, although she didn't feel it, and as far as she was concerned, she was also most definitely not a cat lady, despite her being owned by a demanding and possessive Siamese.

Once she had settled in, she'd pop round and introduce herself to her neighbours. It had been hard to be sociable with the those who lived around her when she was in Bristol because she'd worked shifts. She'd found that people tended to keep themselves to themselves in cities, which also made making friends with the neighbours more difficult.

Now she had returned to Wales, although not to the same area where she'd been born and bred, she intended to immerse herself fully in the life of the village. It was high time she put down proper roots and she vowed to start with the curtain-twitcher next door.

As she followed the cautiously exploring Siamese, Sylvia making her slow way across the lawn, Nessa let herself imagine shared natters over the fence, invites for coffee and barbeques, borrowing cups of sugar, taking in parcels for each other, and watering each other's plants during holidays away. All the things that good neighbours did but had been sadly missing in her life until now.

Once the removal men were finished, Nessa decided her first task was to deep clean the kitchen and find a place for all her equipment. Afterwards, she'd pay a visit to the nearest shop, stock up on supplies, then come back home and bake a couple of cakes, one for each of the neighbours on either side of her.

Ooh, she already knew she was simply going to love living here!

Chapter 3

George

Drat! The woman had caught him looking. George knew he shouldn't have moved a fold in the net curtain to get a better view, but he'd done so anyway, because he'd been certain the woman standing on next door's lawn was the same one whose path he'd been blocking when she'd wanted to enter Pins to Elephants, and he wanted to make sure.

Without a couple of layers of heavy polyester lace in the way, he saw he was indeed correct.

He shrank back, even though he knew she couldn't see him, and waited until she looked away, before he moved closer to the window once more to study her.

She appeared to be on her own and he wondered if there was a husband or partner on the scene.

He hoped not. Two people living next door was double the trouble one would prove to be. Double the noise, double the comings and goings. At least she didn't seem to have any children living with her, he surmised, from the items the removal men were unloading. From his estimate of her age, he thought any offspring she had would probably be of the grown-up variety. How old *was* she, George wondered, squinting at Ms Millbrook, wondering if his initial assessment was correct. He wasn't good with women's ages. He wasn't good with women in any capacity, if he was honest. They were strange, chatty creatures with a tendency to talk too much and a penchant for soft furnishings and sticking their noses in where they weren't wanted.

Men were much easier. All they wanted was to talk about was rugby, the weather and the occasional comment about DIY. He could handle that. Just.

Continuing his scrutiny, he thought once again how attractive she was, although why she had a cat on a lead was anyone's guess.

Great. Trust him to have an odd-bod move in next door. He just hoped she'd keep her oddness to herself and not try to involve him in any strange shenanigans, such as speaking to him or expecting him to be friendly.

He would put up with having a quick chat if he met her in the village, in the same way he exchanged pleasantries with the likes of Sid and Donald, but he could hardly speak to her in the newsagents then ignore her when she wanted to gossip over the fence. So it might be better for everyone concerned if he ignored her completely. All the time. Maybe a brief nod would be acceptable and he might even manage to say 'hello', but a full-blown conversation was out of the question.

The one consolation was that she would probably only occupy her property for a few weeks of the year and the occasional weekend, so he wouldn't have to endure her presence for long.

Unable to drag himself away from the goings-on outside, George continued to watch, careful not to touch the curtain again. He didn't want her to think he was the remotest bit interested, because he wasn't – not at all. But all the racket and the busyness of a couple of men shuffling up and down the drive with assorted sticks of furniture and cardboard boxes didn't make for an atmosphere conducive to a calm working environment. Luckily, he didn't have set hours, and in theory could please himself. Right at this moment, however, George wasn't in the least bit pleased. If this to-ing and fro-ing carried on for much longer, he may have to consider working past his normal clocking-off time, and that simply wouldn't do. He had his afternoon constitutional to take.

Muttering darkly, he checked the time.

They'd been at it for over an hour. He wished they'd get a move on so he could have his breakfast. How much stuff did this woman have? And what could possibly be left in the back of that van?

George gazed in fascination as a washing machine was brought out, followed by a wooden bench. And when the removal men disappeared from view around the side of the cottage, he guessed they were taking the seat into the garden and he hurried to his kitchen at the rear of the bungalow. It was a tight squeeze to get from the doorway to the kitchen window without risking everything toppling over because of those neatly collapsed and stacked boxes on the floor, but he managed it.

Unfortunately, his shed and the garden with its over-grown bushes and shrubs (on his new neighbour's side, not his) obscured his view. He'd be able to see better if he were to go into *his* garden, but he dismissed the idea as being ridiculous, so he returned to the sitting room once more, and continued his vigil at the window.

Nessa Millbrook – he remembered her name – was still there, with her cat on its lead, looking silly. Her, not the cat, he clarified to himself, although the cat didn't appear too happy about being restrained. It was a sleek, creamy-coloured thing with sooty ears, face, tail and paws. From the depths of his mind he dragged out the information that it was most likely to be a member of the Siamese breed, but that was as far as his knowledge of felines went – he wasn't a cat person. Neither was he a dog or any other kind of person, including people. He was perfectly happy in his own company, thank you. Of course, he missed his father, but considering no one could replace him, there didn't seem any point in trying to force the square peg of an acquaintance into the round hole in his heart, a hole which his father had left when he had passed on.

George squinted harder. The cat had moved to explore the full extent of the garden and as his new neighbour came nearer he tried to remember what Mrs Hayworth had said about Nessa Millbrook being from England. Therefore, he expected to hear an English accent of one kind or another, but he was surprised to hear lilting Welsh tones coming out of her mouth as she spoke to her cat – a contrast to the soft West Country burr he'd heard from the removal men.

So, she was Welsh, was she? Interesting.

It certainly put a new perspective on things; namely was she a second-homer or not? His heart sank at the thought of the house next door being occupied full-time. He'd become too accustomed to his isolation and to have it violated now didn't sit well with him. His bungalow might be detached and it might be at the very edge of the village, but having someone else living so near made him feel hemmed in and overlooked.

Vowing to have absolutely nothing whatsoever to do with Ms Millbrook, George finally stepped away from the window. He had better things to do with his day than spend it gawking at his new neighbour.

Realising he had yet to put away his purchases from this morning, he picked the newspaper and radio up from where they'd been sitting on his desk. He then went into the hall and stood on tiptoe to place the neatly folded and unread newspaper on one of the piles, noting with faint alarm that he probably only had a few more months of daily papers to go before that particular stack reached the ceiling and he'd have to start a new one. The reason for the alarm was because there was no room in the hall for another stack. He could barely open his front door as it was, and at the thought of this impending predicament, mild panic fluttered in his chest.

Edging past the other stacks of equally pristine and unread newspapers, careful not to touch them in case they wobbled, George made his precarious way into the kitchen. Once there, he removed the radio from the paper bag and put it to one side whilst he meticulously straightened out any creases in the bag, before folding it and carrying it into his bedroom where he placed it in a cardboard box which sat on top of three other cardboard boxes that were filled to the brim with other assorted paper bags.

Then he returned to the kitchen and gave his attention to the radio itself, removing it carefully from the box, which he saved. He also saved the plastic bag protecting the device, the twist tie around the cord and the little piece of cardboard that covered the plug.

George never threw anything away. Ever.

His father had taught him that. He'd saved everything, no matter how trivial or inconsequential, because one never knew when it might come in handy.

The only thing George threw out were food scraps, because he simply didn't know what to do with them or how to store them. He did, however, make sure to put them in the little green caddy the council had provided to all households for food waste, so he hoped his meagre offerings were being made use of, like fed to pigs or something. The thought of them simply being thrown away set his teeth on edge.

He'd take the radio into the living room and plug it in shortly, but first he needed a cup of tea and a slice of toast before he began work on Mr Ferry's accounts. He was considerably behind in his schedule, but he had to have his breakfast, although he would be eating it later than normal.

Automatically he checked his watch, absently noting that in five minutes it would have been time to give his father his tablet, had he still been alive. As George waited for the kettle to boil and the toast to pop, he marvelled that he was still controlled by the rigid clock of yesteryear, when his whole existence used to revolve around his father's complex needs and wants.

After his father had passed away George had stuck to the same routine, initially because he was too numb to alter it. Later, he continued to stick with it because it suited him just fine. The routine had worked when his father had been alive, and it worked now he was no longer here. To alter it would merely be change for change's sake, and would add no real value to his life, so George kept to his schedule, minus the tablet-giving and the other essential things he used to do for his father.

His was a quiet and measured existence, and that was just the way he liked it.

Feeling thirsty, he fetched his mug from the draining board where it lived, but as he placed it on the only clear area of worktop, he noticed a hairline crack down the side.

Damn! How had that happened? He was always so careful with his things.

With an annoyed sigh, he put it in the washing machine with the other broken mugs, noting there was still room in there for a few more. Not that he intended to add to their number, but despite his best intentions the collection of damaged crockery steadily grew. The corner of the counter next to the wall was devoted to them, as was the cupboard above it, and now the washing machine below. The mugs were his – the delicate china plates, cups and saucers sitting in their midst were his mother's. Most of them were mismatched, which was why they were there – the rest were damaged, and some were in several fragments. Those he'd placed inside a larger cup, making sure to keep all the pieces together.

As with the stacks of newspapers in the hall, the washing machine was filling up relentlessly, but George's more immediate problem was how he was going to manage without his morning tea. Should he go back out?

But he never went back out. He went out twice a day; once before breakfast and once before dinner. That was it.

Although if he didn't have his tea, he couldn't have his toast. And speaking of toast, he'd have to throw this slice out, because it had leapt out of the toaster while he'd been lamenting the demise of his mug and had subsequently gone cold.

He'd use a glass, that's what he'd do. It wasn't ideal but it meant he could get on with his morning. He knew he'd fret either way, so he may as well fret and have his tea and toast.

His mother had been a fretter. It ran in the family. Over the years, she had passed her penchant for fretting onto his father. And now it was George's turn to fret. Any deviation from his daily routine vexed him, occasionally to the point of being unable to function. It was rare, but it had happened, and he prayed it wouldn't happen today. So far it was shaping up to be a truly vexatious day, what with having to buy a new radio, having to make do with a glass for his morning tea and prepare another slice of toast, all the while dealing with the knowledge he had new neighbours.

George felt a headache coming on and he hastened to re-establish control. The cold toast was thrown out of the window for the birds to fight over, the kettle was re-boiled, and he fetched his glass from the draining board.

The draining board usually contained one mug (sadly now relegated to the washing machine), one glass, one dinner plate, one side plate, one bowl, one fork, one knife, one tablespoon and one teaspoon. It used to hold a saucepan and frying pan, too, but that was before the cooker became swamped by flattened cardboard boxes and he could no longer reach it. Or see it. The only bit of it visible beneath its cardboard cloak was a sliver of oven door handle.

The inability to scramble an egg had caused him to fret for days, until he'd read it was possible to use a mug and a microwave – so that's what he now did, and jolly successful it had been, too.

The kettle knocked itself off when it reached the required temperature, and George opened the fridge. The shelves were crammed with empty yoghurt pots, but the compartment inside the door held cheese, butter, milk, a couple of slices of ham and three eggs.

He shook the bottle of milk. It contained enough for one cup of tea and no more, and he berated himself for not purchasing another. It had clean gone out of his head, replaced by the need to buy a new radio. Drat. Now he'd have to go without his mid-morning cup of tea. Could this day get any worse?

The toaster startled him, jerking him out of his thoughts, and with just enough clear space in which to put the final touch to his breakfast, George smeared a thin film of Porter's Pride Organic Welsh Butter, the slightly salted version, onto the warm toast and propped his back against the wall to eat it. In lieu of a suitable table and chair, it was the best he could manage, and he certainly wasn't going to risk taking his meal into the sitting room and dropping crumbs everywhere. His work area was sacred, and he intended to keep it that way.

Breakfast finished, George eyed the empty milk carton. He couldn't leave it there, cluttering up the only available surface in the whole of the kitchen, so he grabbed it and made his way back through the hall, out of the front door and around the side of the bungalow.

Hidden between the garage and the shed was the milk-bottle pile. The plastic bottles didn't stack well, no matter whether they were upright or on their sides, and many had slithered onto the path, which was a worry because the path was visible from the garden next door if anyone stood in the correct position and at the right angle. An empty cottage hadn't been an issue, but now someone had bought it, George feared they might notice, and that would never do. He wished he could get more of those annoying plastic cartons in the shed, but it was so full he was scared to open the door.

Gingerly, he added the bottle to the pile and went back indoors, finally ready to begin work.

Easing himself into the small space where his chair and computer were stationed, he took one final look out of the living-room window and was pleased to see the removal men and their van had gone. Feeling slightly better, he plugged the new radio in and prepared to do battle with Mr Ferry's accounts.

But for once, he failed to find solace in the purity of numbers and columns of figures, as his mind was drawn again and again to the knowledge that a stranger was now living in such close proximity that he imagined he could almost hear her breathing.

Chapter 4

Nessa

Nessa surveyed the mountain of boxes in the room she'd decided would be the master bedroom, and groaned. The bed, chest of drawers, bedside table and two substantial wardrobes were in place; all she had to do was fill them, and if she could wave a magic wand and get it done in the blink of an eye, she would. Mess such as this stressed her out, and she knew she wouldn't be able to settle until everything was put away and in its allotted place, even if it took her all night.

And she'd wanted to bake a couple of cakes, too.

Oh, well, she was sure her neighbours wouldn't mind if she was a day late in introducing herself. They might even pop around to hers, instead.

Damn, now she'd thought of it, she decided it was a very real possibility they might.

The bedroom could wait. The downstairs needed her attention. If she were to invite anyone in, and good manners dictated she couldn't leave them standing on the doorstep, she had to make sure those rooms were as pristine as possible.

She was tempted to shove all the downstairs boxes in the pantry and close the door on them, but it wasn't in her nature, so she set to her cleaning with gusto, hoping the old boiler and the rattling, clanking pipes would be able to deal with her demand for hot water as she wiped the walls down, washed the cupboards out and mopped the floor.

As she worked, she kept up a constant stream of chatter with Sylvia, who answered her more often than not. Nessa swore the cat knew what she was saying.

'Now, Sylvia, I'd appreciate it if you didn't get too friendly with the neighbourhood cats,' she said to the Siamese. 'You know what happened last time – I ended up feeding half of Bristol's feline population. Then there was that stray dog you managed to bring home with you. I'm so glad the Dogs Trust found a home for him.' She scrubbed vigorously at a particularly stubborn mark, her nose wrinkling in disgust. 'As it turns out, I could have kept him if I'd have known I'd be buying this place.'

That was the problem – Nessa had a soft spot for a waif and stray, whether they be animal or human. At her retirement party (it seemed such a long time ago now, but it had only been a few months), one of the nicest comments made to her was that it was her compassionate nature which had made her such a good nurse.

She wasn't sure whether it was compassion or simply human decency that made her unable to ignore someone who needed her help. Now and again it had been mistaken for interference, but anything she did or said came from a good place, so she tried not to worry too much if anyone rejected her assistance.

Sylvia had been one such creature, terrified and with a tendency to lash out; but now look at her – the cat hardly left her side and complained loudly if she felt she wasn't receiving enough love and attention.

Such as now.

Despite Nessa talking constantly to her, Sylvia clearly thought she deserved more, and she kept weaving around her legs, or between her arms if Nessa was on her hands and knees with her head inside a cupboard. The cat rubbed her face against her mistress and frequently batted her with a claw-sheathed paw, until Nessa gave in and stroked her.

But as soon as Nessa returned to her task, Sylvia would start again with the weaving, rubbing and batting, issuing little chirps and mews until her human did as the cat commanded. Nessa often felt her animal was the one in charge and not her, because the little creature could wrap Nessa around her paw with just one wide-eyed, soulful stare.

When Nessa had enough of cleaning and the boxes meant for the kitchen had been unpacked and everything put away in their new homes, she decided to take a break. It would definitely take her a couple of days to remember where she'd put things, but she was grubby, tired, thirsty and hungry, and could do with some fresh air. She'd missed lunch and she hadn't brought any fresh food with her.

A stroll into the village would do her good, and allow her to stretch her legs and fill her lungs with something other than the tang of cleaning products. She could grab a snack and a coffee in the cafe she'd spotted when she'd stopped to pick up cat food earlier, and she could buy some provisions from the shop.

Sylvia would have to remain inside, so Nessa found the cat's snuggly bed in the box marked 'Sylvia' and put it in the bedroom. She would be safe in there, with nothing for her to take her annoyance at being abandoned out on. If the cat became cross, she liked to knock things over, so it was lucky Nessa didn't go much for ornaments, but with the bedroom stuff still to unpack Sylvia would just have to curl up and go to sleep.

Nessa locked the front door behind her and slipped the keys into her pocket, feeling the reassuring weight of them. She still had difficulty believing the cottage actually belonged to her; she'd dreamt of owning a little place in the country of her birth for so long, and now that it had finally become a reality she kept on having to pinch herself.

She shot a swift glance over her shoulder as she walked briskly down the path and spotted Sylvia sitting on the windowsill watching her, the cat's mouth opening and closing in silent protest.

There was no movement from the bungalow, however, and neither were there any signs of life from the cottage on the other side of her own. Feeling emboldened, she craned her neck for a better look, but couldn't see anything to give her any insights about either owner.

A short while later Nessa was in the heart of the village and was gazing around her in delight. A tiny village hall stood next to a squat square-towered church, possibly of Anglo-Saxon or Norman origin, which had a graveyard filled with rickety headstones. For such a small place, the village had a decent selection of shops, including a baker, a general store, which, she noticed as she peered in whilst walking past, seemed to stock an adequate selection of foodstuff, plus the Pins to Elephant shop, a chemist and a newsagent. There was also a hairdresser, a charity shop and a fish-and-chip shop.

She was relieved to see a pub, which was delightfully called the Busy Bumble, and a selection of shops which were aimed at the tourist trade, as well as the cafe she'd noted earlier.

'We haven't got a great deal left,' one of the ladies behind the counter in the cafe warned her as Nessa gazed at the board on the wall.

'I missed lunch,' Nessa explained, 'so I was hoping for something more substantial than a scone or a cookie.' The chalkboard menu advertised a range of sandwiches, quiche, soup of the day, jacket potatoes and the daily special, which, Nessa saw, had been chilli and nachos. Her mouth watered at the thought of it. Hot, spicy and filling, it would have hit the spot. 'I don't suppose you've got any chilli left?' she inquired hopefully.

The woman's expression was regretful. 'I do, but it's not enough for a full portion.'

'Can I have it anyway? I'm happy to pay full price for it.'

'How about if I charge you half price, and throw in a crusty roll and some butter?'

'Deal.' Nessa grinned. 'And could I have a strong coffee to go with it?'

'Of course. Take a seat and I'll bring it over when it's ready.'

Nessa sat down. Already she was starting to feel at home in the village. Applewell reminded her of the place she'd grown up. That had been further east, in the valleys of South Wales, and although the landscape differed considerably, the people here seemed just as friendly. As she ate her plate of steaming chilli, a feeling of serenity stole over her.

'On holiday, are you?' the woman asked her when she arrived to clear the table after Nessa had finished her meal.

'No, I've just moved into a house on Oak Lane.'

'That would be Alys Griffiths' old house. She died a while back. It'll be nice to see the place lived in again. I'm Eleri Jones, by the way.'

'Nessa Millbrook.'

'Where have you moved from?' Eleri asked. 'I know I'm being nosey and you can tell me to mind my own business, but you'll be asked this question a lot, and many more, and if you don't tell us stuff we'll make it up.' The woman grinned at her and Nessa had to laugh.

'I've moved from Bristol, but I was born and bred in a little village in the South Wales Valleys.'

'What made you decide to come to Applewell?'

'I've always wanted a cottage by the sea and now I've retired I decided to follow my heart.'

'I'm sorry to be the one to tell you, but you can't see the sea from anywhere in Applewell,' Eleri informed her solemnly.

Nessa smiled. 'I know, but have you seen the prices of properties with a sea view? And two miles is nothing.'

'What did you do before you retired?'

'I was a nurse.'

'Are you married?'

'Not any more.' Her marriage had been brief and unsatisfactory, and had ended nearly twenty years ago.

'Children?'

'No.'

Eleri paused. 'I think that's it for now. But do pop in again, because I'm sure I'll have lots more questions for you,' she beamed at her, then turned to leave.

'Um, can you tell me who lives next door to me?' Nessa said. 'I've yet to meet my neighbours and it would be nice to know a little about them before I go knocking on doors and introducing myself.'

'Well now, you've got Mairi Edwards in the cottage on your right, and George Nightingale in the bungalow on your left. Mairi is elderly, was widowed last year, and is struggling on her own, so she'll be delighted to have a neighbour she can call on. George is an odd one – he lives alone, too, but he keeps himself to himself. He came back to Applewell a good few years ago to look after his dad and has been here ever since. You can set your watch by him; as regular as clockwork, come rain or shine, he walks down the high street. I've just this minute seen him go past the window.'

'I thought I'd bake a cake for each of them and take them round later.'

Eleri snorted. 'Good luck with George. He won't take kindly to you knocking on his door. Mairi, on the other hand, will be delighted, but she's visiting her daughter in Swansea and won't be back until tomorrow.'

'Thanks for the info. I'll bake her a fresh one tomorrow.'

Nessa paid for her meal and promised to return shortly, then she made her way along the street to the general store, trying to remember what it was she needed. She already had a bag of flour in one of the cupboards in the cottage, so eggs and butter were on her list, milk of course, bread, some fruit and anything else that caught her eye and wasn't too heavy to carry.

She wandered around the shop, which was much larger than it appeared from the outside, and was pleased to see that most of the things she usually bought were available here. Popping items into her basket, she hefted the weight of a four-pint bottle of milk before deciding one pint was enough to tide her over until tomorrow, when she'd come back to do a larger shop and stock up for the coming week.

She was just about to leave the chiller section when she noticed a nicely dressed gentleman glance at her just as he was about to reach into the fridge. To her surprise, he froze, then gave her a startled look before turning smartly on his heel and hurrying away.

What on earth was all that about, Nessa wondered, trying to remember where she'd seen him before. It was recently, she was certain of it...

Then she had it – she'd seen him in Pins and Elephants that morning. He'd been standing in the doorway and she'd had to ask him to step aside. She'd noticed him staring at her whilst she was in the shop and she'd tried not to stare back, especially since she'd smiled at him and he hadn't smiled back.

He was quite distinguished, she thought, well-dressed, slim and tall, and with a nice face. More than nice, if she was being honest. Good-looking, for an older guy, and she estimated his age to be somewhere between fifty and sixty.

She assumed he was a villager rather than a tourist, because of the way he was dressed, and she hoped she'd bump into him again.

Then she pushed the thought away; he was probably married or in a relationship, and she'd only just begun her new life in Applewell – it was far too soon to be thinking about having a relationship of her own. Besides, she was content just the way she was.

Forcing herself to think about the tasks she wanted to do when she arrived home, Nessa pushed the man and his slightly odd behaviour to the back of her mind. She had a house to sort out, cakes to bake, a visit to make and no time to waste.

Chapter 5

George

Damn and blast! The very person George hadn't wanted to meet on his afternoon constitutional earlier had been standing in front of the milk section, so he'd had no choice but to dash off. He had intended on having a quick look around the store to see if there was anything he fancied for his supper, and he hadn't managed to buy any milk, either. He'd have to buy it from the newsagents, which irked him somewhat because he only visited that particular establishment in the morning.

Thankfully, he'd already chosen a new mug, purchased from Pins to Elephants, which he'd carefully placed in his canvas shopping bag, so all he had to do was to dash into the newsagents, grab some milk, and hurry off home before he caught sight of Nessa Millbrook again. It would be simply awful if he bumped into her as he walked back. She might expect to walk with him.

Disconcertingly, somehow the idea appealed to him, and he was so shocked at the mental image of the two of them making the journey home together, that he wondered if he was coming down with a bug. It was so unlike him to be companiable, that he thought about stocking up on cold and flu medicine just in case. He mentally scolded himself for having such a silly notion about his neighbour. He didn't want to talk to Nessa, and he certainly didn't want to take a stroll with her.

The newsagent didn't stock anything suitable for supper, so George snatched a bottle of milk out of the chiller, paid for it while ignoring Sid's raised eyebrows, and marched up the road. He'd have to make do with a tin of macaroni cheese and some bread and butter. Hardly substantial, but he was used to that. He couldn't remember the last time he'd cooked a proper meal. Long before the cooker's hob and oven became unusable and unreachable, he suspected. Maybe even before his father had passed on. The last few months of his father's life had seen the old man's appetite dwindle until he had been eating nothing more than a few mouthfuls of soup or mashed potato (the kind out of a packet), and George had even resorted to feeding him jars of baby food to get some nourishment into him.

It had all been in vain, but he'd had to try.

As soon as he arrived home, George changed out of his shirt, trousers, jacket and tie into more casual clothes. Before he warmed up his macaroni and cheese, he popped into the garden to check on the washing and was pleased to feel that the socks, underpants, shirt and towel which he'd hung out this morning were dry. Unpegging them, he was about to go back indoors when he glanced at the cottage.

She was inside. Nessa. He couldn't see what she was doing, but she was in the kitchen. Worried she might look out of her window and see him staring at her, he gave himself a shake and hastened down the path, anxious to reach the safety of his own kitchen.

Damn – one of the slippery skittish plastic bottles was in the way, and his foot came down on it. It skidded out from underneath the sole of his slippers, but not before he lost his balance. With a cry, he fell sideways into the wall, banging his arm and shoulder and nearly dropping his washing.

Look what she'd made him do, he thought crossly. She'd only moved in a few hours ago and she was already causing problems.

He righted himself and stood there for a moment surveying the ever-growing avalanche of milk bottles. They were trying to take over the path leading to the front of the bungalow, which had become his only way in and out of the garden now that the door from the kitchen to the garden was blocked from the inside by cardboard boxes.

Maybe he could cut the plastic bottles in half to store them – but it would be defeating the object of hanging onto them, because if he did that, then what could they possibly be used for if they were damaged?

This new development with the milk bottles was a concern on two fronts: firstly he had to make sure the path stayed clear, otherwise how else was he going to get into his garden, and secondly, what if *she* noticed?

It hadn't been so much of a worry when the cottage was unlived in, and Mairi Edwards, who lived next door down again, didn't have a clear view of his garden. But the back garden and upstairs windows of the cottage next door was a different matter, and he hoped Nessa Millbrook couldn't see anything she shouldn't from hers.

A shiver of unease travelled down his back. His predictable routine had already suffered at the hands of that woman, he'd only have a tin of macaroni cheese for his supper, he'd almost fallen, and he was fast running out of storage room, as the incident with the plastic bottles showed. What next?

An unusual and troubling sensation swept over him and he had an awful feeling things were starting to spiral out of control.

Annoyed and disturbed, George kicked the offending bottle out of the way. It skittered across the concrete path, the noise making the hairs on the back of his neck stand on end. Unnerved, he scurried around to the front of the house, making sure to close the garden gate so the encroaching bottles didn't follow him. He darted through the front door, automatically twisting sideways to ensure he didn't make contact with the towers of newspapers. If any of them were to topple, he didn't know what he'd do.

Leaning against his front door, he panted slightly, his pulse surging in his ears, apprehension making him jittery. He stayed that way until his breathing slowed, the fear receded and he was able to think about making supper.

He wasn't hungry, but he always made supper at this time and it would probably be best if he tried to eat it, although the thought of tinned macaroni made his stomach churn.

He was right, he discovered, when he came to eat it – he hadn't been hungry, and he threw most of the unappetising pale mushy mess into the bin which he kept purely for food scraps. He'd put it out on Thursday when the rubbish collection was due. There was never a great deal in there. He ate most of what was on his plate because he abhorred waste. But however much he hated throwing food out, today he simply hadn't been able to manage to eat.

Whilst he was rinsing out the empty macaroni tin which he was about to put with the rest of the tins in what had once been his parents' bedroom, there was a knock on the door.

George froze.

A tic began in the corner of his right eye and his stomach did a nasty slow roll.

Of course, he wouldn't answer it. He never did unless he was expecting a parcel, and it was too late for a delivery driver or the postman. No one else came to his door. No one ever called, therefore he never expected anyone. The last time someone knocked on his door had been during the lead-up to the last round of local government elections a few years ago. He'd not answered it then either, and had added the flyer which had been pushed through his letterbox to the pile in the spare room, unread. It was still there.

Instead, he wove his way to the sitting room, squashed himself between the dresser and the armchair once more, and peered out of the window. He could see his front door quite clearly, as the bungalow was an L shape with the main entrance in the corner of the two wings. He could also see who was standing there, holding a large round tin in her hands and wearing an expectant expression on her face.

Nessa Millbrook!

The woman was a menace, but even as irritation swept over him, a part of him was intrigued – what on earth did she want?

He shrank back, praying he hadn't been seen. Not that it was easy to see anything beyond the nets (he knew, because he'd made sure of it) but a waft of air might have caused them to move and he didn't want her to realise he'd heard her knock.

George studied her as she patiently stood there, two paces back from his step, and he wondered why she was carrying a tin and why she was bothering him. If she wanted to borrow a cup of sugar, then she was out of luck – he didn't have any. And if he did, he wouldn't lend it to her because then she'd have an excuse to knock his door again in order to return it.

He didn't want a friendship with his neighbour. Heck, he didn't even want to make eye contact, so the thought of holding a conversation with her made his toes curl.

When he failed to answer, she moved closer to the glass panel in the door and tried to peer through it. Luckily it was frosted, but when she was unable to satisfy her nosiness, he had an awful thought she might head for the window he was behind and try to look through that instead.

She didn't. She merely bent down and placed the tin on his step. Then, with a final glance at the door, she turned and headed back down his drive.

He watched her until she entered her own front garden, trotted up the path and disappeared inside her house.

George was sorely tempted to go and see what she'd left for him, but he waited a while, like an animal wary of a trap, just in case she was watching for him to emerge, ready to pounce.

And he was glad he did, because less than a minute later, she was hurrying down her drive again and onto his, a piece of paper in one hand and a pebble in the other.

Bemused and more than a little curious, he saw her place the piece of paper on the tin and put the pebble on the top of it.

Then he watched as she went back into her own house once more.

This time, she didn't re-emerge, even though he waited until the light bled from the sky and his legs began to ache from standing still for so long.

Finally, he plucked up the courage to retrieve the tin.

When he opened the door a crack, he hunkered down on his haunches and stuck his arm through the gap. He felt around, then stretched further, his cheek up against the doorframe as he groped on the ground.

There it was!

Carefully, he pulled the round tin towards him until it was close enough to risk opening the door a little wider. He grasped it with both hands, and as soon as it was inside he slammed the door shut in relief.

He read the note.

Just a little something from me to you to say 'hi'.

> *Your new neighbour,*
> *Nessa x*
> *(Nessa Millbrook)*

He read it again, perplexed. Why would she say hello in a note? Was the 'x' supposed to be a kiss? Why would she do that when she hadn't even met him? And what was the little something she was referring to?

There was only one way to find out – he'd have to open the tin.

But why did he feel that opening it would be akin to lifting the lid on Pandora's box? Feeling foolish, because there was hardly likely to be a ticking bomb inside, George prised it open and his nose was assaulted by the most delicious aroma of freshly baked cake. He identified vanilla

39

and strawberry before his tummy clenched in hunger and he realised he simply had to have a slice right now.

He didn't care that the woman whom he'd vowed to have absolutely no contact and nothing to do with had given it to him. All he could think about was the anticipated sweetness exploding on his tongue.

Tempted to lift the cake out of the tin whole and take a bite there and then, George wrestled with his manners, despite having nobody to see or to censure him, and took the cake into the kitchen before cutting himself a large slice.

The first mouthful almost made him cry. It was as if he'd just tasted every birthday cake his mother had ever made for him. Victoria sponge, that's what it was called, and she'd baked one on his birthday every year without fail for as long as he could remember.

Until her diagnosis, that is, and she'd become too ill, and then the baking, along with everything else she'd done, had stopped.

That was the last time anyone had baked anything for him. In fact, it was probably the last time he'd tasted proper homemade cake. Until now.

It was the buttercream that did it, the creamy sweet filling sending his taste buds into overdrive, the floral sweetness of the jam following hot on its heels.

He ate the slice in less than two minutes.

Then he cut another piece and ate that, too.

Before greed could overwhelm him again, he wrapped the remainder in one of the plastic bags salvaged from something or other, he couldn't remember what, and stowed it carefully in the fridge. He had to remove several empty and flattened orange juice cartons to do so, but the occasion warranted it. He'd return them to their rightful place once the cake was eaten.

He'd also return the empty tin to its owner as soon as it grew dark, because he didn't like the thought of it sitting there on the small space in front of the microwave. It didn't belong in his house, and he had the feeling it was watching him, as though it had been sent to spy on him and report back.

A movement just outside the window made him look up, and to his immense consternation George realised he was being watched.

The cat whom he'd last seen tethered to the end of a red leather leash, was now sitting on his kitchen windowsill and staring in at him, despite the net curtain. It appeared to be observing him in much the same way as he imagined it might look at a mouse – all pricked ears and intensity, tinged with mild disdain and a smidgeon of curiosity.

'Shoo,' he hissed at it, flapping his arms in a go-away motion. 'Scat.'

He wasn't entirely certain whether the cat could see inside or not, but it gave him a long, level cat-stare before it rose gracefully to its feet, held its tail high, then turned its back to give him a view of its bottom, before jumping to the ground and disappearing from view.

He hoped this wasn't going to become a habit. If so, he'd have to break his vow and have words with Ms Millbrook.

He was going to have to have words with her, anyway; good manners dictated he should thank her for the cake. That he didn't want to, was neither here nor there.

How sneaky and conniving of her. He now had no choice; he had to speak to her.

But – and here was an idea – he could do the same thing as she had done; he'd write a note of thanks on the back of the one she'd sent him and place it on top of the cake tin when he returned it later.

Genius!

So that was exactly what he did, and when he crept back into his own house much later that night, he treated himself to a third piece of cake.

It worried him a little that he was deviating from his routine, as he made it a rule never to snack after he'd had supper, but he could hear the sponge calling to him and he was unable to resist. Besides, the small amount of macaroni cheese he'd consumed could hardly warrant the accolade of supper. Therefore, the cake *was* his supper, and the fact he'd taken the better part of three hours to eat it was of no consequence.

The cake was the only highlight in what had been a quite disturbing day.

Chapter 6

Nessa

Where on earth was Sylvia? Nessa had searched the cottage and was fairly convinced the cat wasn't in it. But then again, the naughty little thing had been known to hide then watch as her mistress frantically looked for her.

Cats, as Nessa well knew, could hide in the smallest and most inaccessible of places – the kind of places you'd look at and think, 'nah, no cat would ever fit in there'. But they would and they did. And they probably took great delight in watching their owners run around like headless chickens trying to find them.

It was only when she heard the cat meowing loud enough to wake the dead outside the door leading to the rear garden, that Nessa realised Sylvia must have somehow slipped out when she went to introduce herself to her neighbour in the bungalow.

'You naughty girl,' she told Sylvia, who didn't seem to care a jot that she wasn't supposed to be outside yet in case she got lost. The cat chirruped as Nessa let her in and proceeded to wind herself around Nessa's legs, undoubtedly begging for food.

'Where have you been, eh? Exploring your new territory? You're lucky you didn't get lost.' Nessa stroked the cat's silken head and received a loud purr in return.

43

Relieved that Sylvia was inside because it was starting to get dark, Nessa switched on a lamp in the living room and drew the curtains. The room was more or less arranged to her satisfaction now. Everything had been unpacked and put in its place, although whether every object would stay in its original position was another matter. She'd live with it for a while, and see whether the room worked the way it was or whether she'd decide to change it.

Curious to see if her cake offering had been accepted, she peered out of her living-room window, and noticed the tin was no longer on George Nightingale's doorstep. A feeling of satisfaction stole over her. Eleri had told her he wouldn't take kindly to her knocking on his door, but he seemed to have taken kindly to the cake. He'd taken it inside, at least.

Or maybe he hadn't been pleased by the offering and the cake was residing in the bottom of his bin at this very moment. Her satisfaction gave way to doubt. It would be such a shame not to get on with one of her neighbours.

She'd try anew with Mairi Edwards. From what Eleri had told her, the old lady was lonely and would welcome some company.

For now though, she needed to focus on getting her bed made and her clothes put away. To be fair, there wasn't a great deal left to be done – the downstairs was tidy and neat, and her bedroom would soon be the same. Nessa was tired, it had been a long and exciting day, but she had an hour or so left in her, and she intended to make full use of it, knowing she wouldn't be able to truly rest until everything was shipshape.

She was upstairs, busily straightening the pillows inside their recently purchased cases in honour of her new house, when she heard a faint noise coming from outside.

It wasn't completely dark yet, but it was not far off it, and the silence surrounding the cottage was quite profound: no traffic, no voices, no music. Just the occasional breath of wind sighing through the trees and the distant lowing of a cow. It was a calm refreshing change from the hectic noisy city she was accustomed to. Maybe in time the quiet would grate on her nerves or she might find it disturbing, but for the moment she relished it.

Until, that is, she heard an odd sound coming from outside again.

She'd already closed her bedroom curtains (old habits died hard) and she'd switched the ceiling light on in order to work better, so, conscious she might make a shadow on the fabric, Nessa scuttled around the bed and sidled across to the window, keeping both her and her shadow close to the wall. Then she gently eased the curtain to one side and peeped out.

It had probably been a fox. Or maybe a badger. Were there any badgers nearby? Hedgehogs could be quite noisy...

It was none of those things, she realised, when she met the startled gaze of a man.

The man was hurrying down her path, glancing over his shoulder as he did so and looking extremely furtive.

His eyes widened when he saw her. She was certain hers did, too, because she had no doubt the man was George Nightingale. He stumbled, caught his balance, then high-tailed it back to his own house.

She was also in no doubt George Nightingale was the same man she'd encountered in the general store earlier today. The same man who'd taken one look at her and scarpered.

Wondering what she possibly could have done to offend him – she'd only moved in today, for goodness' sake! – she hurried downstairs, guessing she'd find her cake tin on her doorstep. Whether it would be full, was something else she had to know.

When she opened the door, it was to discover her guess had been correct. Her tin was there, complete with the note and the pebble on top.

Except, the note wasn't in her handwriting. It was written in a neat, spikey hand, unlike her rounded, feminine script.

Thank you.

George Nightingale

She noticed with a bemused smile that it was succinct. No kissy x, and just the briefest of content. But at least he had thanked her, and he needn't have done so. If he hadn't responded, she would have taken the hint and left well enough alone. But he had, and he'd also removed the cake from the tin.

She'd have him smiling at her over the hedge before too long, and she might even get a 'hello' out of him – if he didn't scurry off the next time she saw him, that is.

And she was certain he'd been inside the bungalow when she'd dropped the cake off. She didn't know why she thought this, she just did. Call it a gut feeling, but she felt like she was being watched.

It hadn't made her feel uncomfortable.

It had, however, made her feel a little sad that the man who lived next door had felt he needed to hide.

He was scared of something, that much was obvious, but of what, she had no idea.

She intended to find out, and if she could help, then she would. She might be retired, but she was still a nurse, and there was something about the man next door that told her he needed her help just as much as if he had appeared in the emergency room.

To Nessa, the fact that George quite possibly didn't realise he needed her help, was of no consequence whatsoever.

Chapter 7

Nessa

Birdsong woke Nessa the next morning, swiftly followed by Sylvia growling and chattering.

She sat up and sleepily regarded her cat, who was perched on the windowsill, her head poking through the gap in the curtains, uttering threats at the feathery things outside. When Nessa dragged herself out of bed and had a look at what Sylvia was so perturbed about, it was to see several blackbirds busily pecking at the lawn.

Sylvia gave her a huge-eyed stare for a moment, then turned her attention back to the birds.

'You can have some breakfast,' Nessa told her, 'but you can't go out. Not yet. It's too soon.'

The cat mewed at her and jumped down off the sill as though she knew exactly what Nessa had said. And maybe she did, Nessa thought as she swished the curtains open and gazed at the view. It was going to be a glorious day. The sun rose behind the cottage and the sky to the west was blue and clear with only a hint of cloud.

She knew West Wales was famed for its rainfall as well as its scenery, so she decided to make the most of the good weather and walk to the coast. As she'd told Eleri in the cafe yesterday, two miles was nothing; Nessa used to walk at least three times that amount during the course of one shift at work, or so her Fitbit had told her.

And there wasn't a great deal left to do in the cottage. Thanks to her minimalist lifestyle and a savage declutter before moving day, Nessa hadn't brought an excessive amount with her from her house in Bristol. Her one weakness was books, but she knew if she began to unpack the books currently stacked in boxes in the spare bedroom, she'd be unable to resist opening their pages, and before she knew it, the whole day would have disappeared. So she decided to save that treat for a rainy day.

Sylvia duly fed, Nessa took her own breakfast into the garden. She'd brought a bench with her and a little patio set, consisting of a wrought iron table and two chairs, which she'd asked the removal men to pop on the paved area just outside the kitchen door. The bench had been put at the top of the garden.

As she sat there, chewing her toast, she studied the garden. It was overgrown and the lawn had become a meadow of sorts, the bench half-buried in the long grass. She quite liked the look of it, and considered mowing a path through the grass instead of decimating all of it. The bushes would need to be trimmed back though, as they were encroaching into the garden and she had a feeling the space would be significantly larger if they were brought under control.

With the early morning sun on her face, the temperature was rising nicely, and it was deeply pleasant sitting there without having to rush off to work, or spend her precious time off doing domestic chores. After her walk, Nessa planned to take the car into the village for supplies of fresh food, then she intended to come back out here with a book and a cuppa and simply enjoy the freedom.

No doubt she'd get bored with a lack of direction in her life and a lack of structure to her day, but for now she intended to luxuriate in it. She almost felt as though she were on holiday, and that this cottage was rented for a week. Nessa wanted to pinch herself because she still couldn't believe she actually lived here.

A noise had her cocking her head to the side as she tried to identify where it came from, before she realised it was the sound of a door closing. It was swiftly followed by footsteps and she guessed her neighbour was on the move.

'All right, George?' a man's voice called from the lane. 'Off into the village, are you?'

'That's correct.'

'I'm just taking Jim for a walk.'

'So I see.'

'Met your new neighbour yet?'

'Not yet.' George's voice was growing fainter, and Nessa guessed he must have continued to walk on down the lane as the strange man's voice grew louder by the same degree.

She'd have to rectify her neighbour not having met her properly yet, she thought with a smile as she got ready for her walk.

After saying goodbye to Sylvia, who glared at her balefully, Nessa tripped down her garden path and practically skipped along the lane, making for a kissing gate set on the edge of a field which sported a sign above it indicating it was a public footpath. It seemed to be heading in the right direction, so she thought she'd follow it and hope it led her to the sea.

This part of Wales was hilly but not too mountainous, with open fields, hedgerows and farmland, and she knew from previous visits to the area when she was looking for a property to buy, that the coastline was a concertina of dramatic windswept cliffs and sheltered hidden valleys leading to secret beaches and tiny coves. Nessa was hoping the path would take her to one of these, or at least intersect the coastal path which ran along the whole of the Welsh coastline, dipping down into bays and meandering through towns and villages. Once she was on that, she'd be able to follow it for a while until she found a beach she could access. Some of the coves were at the base of those cliffs and were only accessible from the water, and she knew that around October, seals hauled themselves out of the sea to give birth to their pups on those beaches. But there were secluded beaches that it *was* possible to walk down to, and Nessa was hoping to discover one of those; she had a hankering to feel some sand between her toes and sea spray in her hair.

The footpath traced its way around the edge of a field filled with stubble from a crop long harvested, before heading due west. It was slightly muddy underfoot, and she could see footprints and pawprints where the earth was especially soft, but she met no one. Her only companions were the sparrows chirping furiously from the tall hedgerows and the occasional blackbird perched high on a branch, his song proclaiming this territory was his. Other small birds flitted and fluttered, and she tried to identify them but failed. However, she did recognise the crows overhead from their raucous calls, and as she neared the coast she saw whirling seabirds circling high in the sky, and the unmistakable cries of gulls warmed her heart. It was the sound of childhood holidays, and with the sun beating down she really did feel as though she'd been transported back in time fifty years – all she needed was a bucket and a net, and a few hours to clamber over the rocks to examine the contents of the inevitable rock pools.

Her first sight of the sea sent her into raptures, and Nessa checked her watch. Forty-seven minutes had brought her across two fields and within spitting distance of the coastal path. She went through another kissing gate, and she was there, standing on a clifftop with the Irish Sea disappearing into the hazy distance.

She took a deep breath of salt-tanged air and filled her lungs with its freshness, the westerly wind carrying the scent of the open ocean and blowing her hair away from her face.

She was anxious not to deviate from the path because of the incredibly steep drop, but from what she could see, the cliff face was crowded with hundreds of nesting birds. The air was filled with their calls. Taking extreme care, Nessa moved closer to the edge and looked down to see the waves pounding rhythmically against the rocks, sending white plumes of spray tens of feet into the air, and the boom of it reverberated through her chest.

On a calm, sunny day like today, the scene was awe-inspiring enough – but imagine what it would be like in wilder weather, she thought. She intended to enjoy the rainy, stormy days just as much as the warm, sunny ones.

For now though, she wanted to feel the chill of the water around her ankles, so she looked to her right, but saw nothing but rocky turrets. To her left however, there was an inlet, so she decided to follow the path in that direction to see if there was a way to get down to the sea.

For the next ten minutes she was certain there wasn't, but when the path dropped down into a valley carved into the hillside, steep and wooded at its base, she saw it was possible to reach a small pebble-and-sand beach. There would be more exploring to be done in the future, as the path carried on up the other side of the cove and along the top of the cliffs opposite, but for today this was far enough.

As soon as she left the clifftop, the wind eased and she realised how sheltered this little piece of paradise was. It was a perfect beach in miniature, with everything she could wish for – rocks still glistening from where the tide had recently receded, there was a strip of dry sand beyond the high-tide mark where the beach met the woodland, and a tiny stream bisected the beach and trickled steadily to meet the sea. It was magical, and Nessa instantly claimed it as her own. She knew she'd spend many a contented hour here with a picnic and a book, and as she gazed around in delight, she felt peace steal over her.

On another visit she would explore the little valley behind and see where it led, but right now all she wanted was to slip off her shoes and head to the waves, which were much calmer in the tiny cove now they no longer had any cliffs to beat into submission.

Dodging rafts of pebbles and sticking to the sandy areas, Nessa made her way to the water's edge, the sand cool under her warm feet, and squealed when her skin was lapped by a particularly determined wave. Ooh, it was cold!

She skipped backwards, giggling, before darting closer again, playing a little game with the waves, just as she used to do as a child. And when she was out of breath and her feet had started to tingle from the cold, she headed up the beach to where she'd left her socks and trainers and sat for a while, letting her toes dry off and warm up in the sun, her face turned skyward and her eyes closed.

Finally, she knew she should make a move. There would be plenty of other days she could spend on the beach, and she wanted to pop into the village to stock her fridge and freezer. Perhaps she could see if the shop where she'd bought the cat food yesterday also sold paint, because every room in her sweet little cottage could do with freshening up. And she also wanted to bake the cake for the woman next door and introduce herself.

Suddenly anxious to get on, she wrestled her damp feet into her socks and shoes, and made her way back up to the clifftop, puffing and panting with the steepness of the climb. With a stiff breeze to cool her, she walked briskly back across the fields, faster this time, and made it back home in forty minutes. Pretty good, she thought, satisfied with her level of fitness for a woman in her fifties. And if she could find a way up through the valley and back into the village, then that circular coastal route could become her daily walk.

As she reached her front door, she automatically glanced at the bungalow.

There was no movement, no indication anyone was in, and nothing to imply George was watching. But she had a feeling he was, and she smiled and waved anyway.

If he wasn't, it wouldn't matter, and if he was, he'd see she was trying to break the ice.

Slow and steady, she told herself as she went inside to be greeted by a loudly protesting Sylvia – she'd wear George down eventually. But what she didn't want to think about in too much depth was her reason for wanting to do so in the first place – because she had a feeling it might be because she was more attracted to him than she cared to admit.

Chapter 8

George

Nessa had seen him again! She must have done, else why would she have waved? He knew it was impossible to see through the net curtains, but it didn't prevent him from thinking she had.

George wished she'd go away. And if that wasn't possible, that she'd just stop bothering him. He'd done nothing to warrant her attention and if there was one thing he detested it was nosey parkers. Why she felt the need to harass him was beyond his comprehension. And he most certainly did feel harassed. In fact, he felt spied on, as though she was watching his every move.

He didn't like it. Not one little bit. At least, that's what he told himself, ignoring the flutter in his stomach when he thought of the smile she'd given him.

Perhaps he shouldn't have returned her tin; but then, she might have come knocking on his door, asking for it back. Maybe he shouldn't have written a thank-you note, although his words had hardly been friendly, just to the point. He'd had nothing else he wanted to say to her, and he hadn't even wanted to say thank you, but he didn't want people thinking he was rude.

George watched her return to her cottage. He'd seen her from quite a distance away, striding across one of John

Porter's fields as if she owned it. He wondered if she'd found the little cove, the one he used to spend all his time in when he was a boy. The secret inlet he'd liked to pretend belonged to him, and was still possessive about even now.

It was years since he'd been there. The last time was before he went to university, when he had been filled with such dread that he wouldn't fit in (he'd been right), consumed with fear of leaving home and brimming with sick excitement at the thought of starting a new life.

The new life had taken him to Liverpool, where he'd struggled dreadfully with being a student, and he'd only felt more at home after he'd obtained his degree and had been offered a job with the Inland Revenue in that very city. And there he'd stayed until his mother's death and his father's increasing dependency had brought him back home.

Of course, he hadn't been forgotten by the village. No matter how far he'd gone or for how long, people remembered him. But on his return he'd kept himself to himself, and gradually he'd faded into the background – which was precisely where he wanted to be – and they left him alone to get on with his life. He could cope with the hellos, and the how-are-yous. But anything more unsettled him.

Nessa Millbrook unsettled him.

And he didn't like it one little bit.

He took a hasty step back, shrinking away from the window as though his neighbour had the ability to see into his very soul. Doing so, he bumped into one of the towering stacks of books, sending the whole lot tumbling to the ground in a cascade of bent spines and knocked corners.

Now look what she'd made him do!

Close to sudden and unwelcome tears, George let out a cry of dismay as he saw the pile next to it wobble, too.

No, no, that wasn't good.

He hurried to steady it, trying not to stand on the paperbacks piled at his feet. Only when he was satisfied nothing else was about to fall over did he relax a fraction, enough to bend down and start restacking what had fallen.

Twenty minutes passed before he'd stretched on tiptoes to balance the final book on the top, careful not to let any of them touch their neighbouring piles, and also careful to place the books square on. He couldn't abide it if they weren't straight. He had promised himself he would sort them out one day, put them in alphabetical order by genre, or by size, but he had so many now that the task would be impossible. He wondered if there was anything on how to deal with nosey neighbours in one of the many psychology books he possessed, but he didn't have the heart to sift through them. He didn't have the room either. The only way into and out of the room was between the stacked piles that Nessa Millbrook had made him knock over. If he wanted to sort them, he'd have to spread the titles out in the narrow corridor between the piles, which would block the way, and he needed to get to his desk by the window or else he wouldn't be able to work, and no work meant no money, and—

George began to hyperventilate, his breath coming in short, sharp gasps, and his pulse pounding in his ears. A headache exploded in his left temple and he suddenly felt sick.

Groping behind his back, he reached for his office chair, the only seat in the whole bungalow which was free from things, and sank into it, his heart thudding so hard he prayed it wouldn't leap out of his chest.

Breathe in, one, two, three; breathe out, one, two, three, he chanted in his head, wishing he had a paper bag to hand. The majority of them were in their designated place in the dining room; the room he could no longer enter because something (many somethings?) had fallen against the door, holding it firmly closed. Thinking about what sort of state the room must be in, the disorganised mess in there, made George gasp once more, and bright spots appeared before his eyes.

Breathe, breathe, breathe…

Gradually, he brought himself under control, but the episode left him shaken and discombobulated. There was no way he could do any work today, not after that. Which meant he'd have not done any work for nearly two whole days – and all because of the woman next door.

Bloody hell, he thought – and he never swore, not even in his head, which gave him an indication of the level of distress he was feeling – what was he going to do?

Chapter 9

Nessa

The more Nessa saw of the village of Applewell, the more she fell in love with it, she reflected, as she walked down the little main street. It had seemed a bit daft to take her car for such a short journey, so she'd decided to walk even though she wouldn't be able to buy as much; but as long as she had something for her tea and a few bits for the freezer, she wouldn't starve. Plus, there was always tomorrow. Nothing was stopping her from taking another stroll into the village in the morning. She smiled to herself; she was so used to dashing from work to home and back again, and fitting shopping in when she could, that she kept forgetting she was out of the rat race now and she could do as she pleased when she pleased.

Not for ever, of course, because the novelty would eventually wear off and she'd get bored, but for now she needed time to catch her breath and take stock. She was certain there was a charity or two she could do some voluntary work for, and as she dawdled through the village she spotted a charity shop in aid of homelessness, which was a matter close to her heart, having treated so many of Bristol's vulnerable people over the years. Maybe she could offer her services once she'd settled in?

With that in mind, she decided to pop into Under-Cover and take a look around. She didn't need anything – far from it – she'd already given a load of stuff to charity before she moved, but it would be nice to get a feel for the place.

'Hiya,' a young woman at the back of the shop called. She was sorting through lengths of curtains and pairing them up.

'Hello.' Actually, now Nessa came to think of it, the curtains on the windows in the cottage were rather thread-bare and dusty. None of the ones at her old place would have fitted, so she'd left them in Bristol. She could do with a couple of new pairs.

'They are pretty,' she said, spying some lightweight cotton ones, which were white with sprigs of lavender with green stems printed on them, and would look perfect in the kitchen.

'Here, take a look; I think they're brand new.' The woman handed them to her.

Nessa took them and held them up. She could tell without knowing the measurements that they wouldn't fit. 'Far too long, I'm afraid,' she said and gave them back.

'You could always shorten them.'

Nessa smiled and shook her head. 'I can barely sew a button on,' she admitted. She might be extremely practical in some areas, but needlework wasn't one of them, despite having sutured hundreds of wounds as part of her role as an Emergency Nurse Practitioner.

'Are you staying in Applewell or are you passing through? Because if you're going to be around for a few more days, I know a lady who would shorten them for you, and it would only take her half an hour.'

'I'm staying, permanently.'

The woman's eyes lit up. 'Are you the lady who bought old Alys Griffiths' house?'

Nessa laughed. 'Guilty as charged.'

'How are you settling in? I'm Catrin, by the way.'

'I'm Nessa, Nessa Millbrook.'

It was Catrin's turn to laugh. 'I know. You can't keep anything quiet in a small place like this.'

'I'm beginning to see that! I'm settling in well, thanks. The cottage is more or less sorted, so I've been exploring this morning. I found the most gorgeous little beach just across the fields from my house.'

Catrin glanced around and hissed, 'Shhh, we try to keep that to ourselves,' even though the shop was empty apart from the two of them.

'Darn it! I thought I was the only one who knew about it,' Nessa joked.

'Seriously, if tourists got wind of how pretty it is, there'd be hundreds of them swarming all over it. Don't get me wrong,' Catrin added hastily, 'tourists are a lifeline for the village, but we do like to keep some things for the locals. Now, about these curtains; what do you say about getting them shortened?'

Nessa had to admire the woman's business acumen. 'I'm not sure…'

'Tell you what, I'll put them to one side, and you can let me know tomorrow if you want them or not. Depending on how much you need off them, you could have the remnants made into cushions.'

'That's a thought. I've got a table and two chairs in my kitchen, and having matching cushions would be great.'

'Gracie won't mind if I give you her number,' Catrin said, scribbling on a sticky note. 'She can tell you how much she charges, and you can decide from there.'

'How much are the curtains?' Nessa asked.

'Five pounds, and cheap at twice the price!'

'OK, thank you. Put them aside, I'll give this lady a call, and I'll let you know tomorrow.'

Nessa left the shop bemused and impressed, both with the prices and with Catrin herself. She was a determined saleswoman, and Nessa was still smiling as she went to the butcher's to buy some beef for the casserole she intended to make for her tea.

It was strange, she mused, as she watched the man wrap the diced meat in paper, how she'd immediately reverted to calling the evening meal 'tea', when she'd always referred to it as 'dinner' in Bristol. Her roots were showing, and Nessa also realised what she had thought was an almost imperceptible Welsh lilt in her voice was becoming more pronounced. She even found herself saying 'diolch' instead of 'thanks', when the butcher swapped over the beef parcel for her money.

He grinned at her and she smiled back. Everyone was so friendly, she thought. Then she sobered a little as she realised not *everyone* was; there was the prickly matter of George next door...

George would have to wait though, because when she arrived home Nessa saw Mairi's windows were open and she guessed her neighbour must have returned from her visit, meaning Nessa had a cake to bake and a visit of her own to make.

Which was why, just over an hour and a half later, Nessa was standing outside Mairi's house with a cake safely nestled in her hands (the same tin she'd left on George's doorstep), wearing a smile on her face.

The door opened on the first knock and Nessa came face to face with a tiny, wizened woman, who had a slight stoop, white frizzy hair and spectacles perched on the end of her nose. She was sporting an answering smile.

'Come in, come in.' Mairi opened the door wider and stepped to the side.

Nessa hesitated, hoping the old dear didn't make a habit of inviting total strangers into her house. 'I'm Nessa, from next door.'

'I know.' Her wrinkled little face creased even more as she beamed at her.

Nessa frowned. 'How—?'

'The Applewell grapevine.'

'But you've only just returned,' Nessa objected, following the diminutive figure down a hall almost identical to the one she herself owned.

'Makes no difference. Word gets about. You can't keep anything secret in this place, so don't even try.' She gestured to one of two armchairs in the kitchen and Nessa sat down, still clutching the tin, while Mairi bustled about filling the kettle and setting out cups and saucers.

Nessa handed her the tin. 'I baked you a cake to say hello.'

'That's very kind of you. I knew I was going to like you.'

'You did?'

Mairi nodded earnestly. 'You've got that kind of face.'

Nessa bit back a smile. 'Thank you. I think.'

'It's a caring face. An open face. Ooh, I'm so glad you moved in next door.' She clapped her hands with childlike glee and Nessa couldn't help grinning. 'It's comforting to have someone living there – it's been empty for far too long.'

Nessa remembered what Eleri had told her about Mairi being lonely, and said impulsively, 'How would you like to pop to mine for tea? I'm making a beef casserole with new potatoes and veg.'

Mairi hesitated.

'You'll be doing me a favour. I always make too much and I hate throwing food out. Besides, I bet you haven't had a chance to go shopping yet.'

'If you're sure?' The old lady continued to look doubtful. 'I was going to have one of my ready meals; I keep a supply of them in my freezer.'

'You can have it another time. Please say yes – I'd love to have some company.'

'In that case, yes, I would love to join you.'

Her eyes had lit up and Nessa nodded to herself. Definitely lonely. Whilst Nessa wouldn't be able to alleviate it entirely, she could help lessen it a little, and she wanted Mairi to know she was there if she needed her. Nessa looked around curiously. The kitchen was rather old-fashioned, with an ancient range in the chimney breast where a fireplace would have once been, and an original butler sink. There were no fitted units; instead, Mairi had a couple of free-standing ones and a large table pushed up against the wall. Along with the armchairs, Nessa thought it looked like something out of a television programme set at around the turn of the last century.

However, it was cosy and had a well-loved feel, and beyond the kitchen the garden was a riot of colour.

'You've got a glorious garden,' she said, as Mairi cut the cake and poured the tea. The old woman was using a teapot and carefully filling the two cups.

'I do, don't I? But it's getting a little wild. Every year it takes more and more effort to keep it looking nice.' Mairi placed the cups and plates on the little table between the two armchairs and sank into the vacant seat with a groan.

'I can help, if you like?'

'Bah, you've got enough to do with your own garden. I can manage.'

Nessa let it go for the time being. She didn't want to force herself on the old lady, but at least she'd made the offer.

'Now, tell me about yourself,' Mairi said, taking a slurp of tea before opening her mouth wide and biting into her large slice of cake. 'Mmm, delicious.' Her voice was muffled by the enormous mouthful.

'I hope my other neighbour liked it as much,' Nessa said worriedly.

Mairi swallowed and licked her lips. 'Did you make one for George, too? That was kind of you.'

Nessa nodded. 'I left it on his doorstep, and he left the empty tin and a note of thanks on mine.'

Mairi pulled a face. 'That sounds like George. I knew him when he was a boy. Odd little thing. Very shy. Extremely polite. I don't think he had many friends. He still doesn't.'

'That's so sad. I wonder why not?'

'I think he was teased a lot in school. Bullying, they'd call it nowadays. His mother had a devil's job to get him to go once he'd started big school at Lampeter and mixed with all those kids from outside Applewell. Children can be so cruel when you don't fit in. He wasn't what you'd call sporty. He liked his books and he was good with numbers. His mother was so proud of him when he went to university. He was the first one in the family to get a degree. That was in something to do with numbers… She did tell me…? No, it's gone. It'll come to me eventually. Anyway, he lived away for years, went to Liverpool, but he came back when her cancer got too much. He had to, because someone had to look after his dad. Parkinson's. Dreadful disease, and Mr Nightingale had always been so good with his hands, too. Could repair anything, that man could. And if you needed anything, he'd have it – my Jim was always popping round for a nail or a bit of string. You name it, Mr Nightingale could lay his hands on it.' She smiled softly. 'I remember going in his garage once and he was servicing his old Morris Minor himself – you could in them days because cars were simpler then, none of this computer rubbish – and his shelves were stacked with jars of nails, screws, washers, all of them neatly labelled and most of them rusty.'

Nessa was fascinated to hear about her elusive neighbour's history, although she felt a little guilty to be gossiping about him. She ate a final mouthful of cake – it was rather good, even though she said so herself – and got up to put her plate in the sink, earning herself a smile from her new friend.

'He was older than me, was Mr Nightingale, by a good few years,' Mairi said, 'and I think he remembered the war and the rationing that went on for years afterwards. Of course, he was only a boy himself then, but he used to say "waste not, want not", and he never threw anything out if it could be used again. I remember my own mother saving the greaseproof paper that the butter used to come in; she used to wipe it over and smooth it out, then lined her baking trays with it. She did that right up until she died.' Mairi sounded wistful, then she seemed to shake herself. 'But, eh, I thought we were talking about you?'

'Sorry. There's not much to say. I recently retired – I used to be a nurse – and I've always wanted to live by the sea, so here I am. And before you say anything, Eleri from the cafe has already pointed out Applewell is two miles inland,' she joked.

'It's as near as dammit, and you can walk there in less than an hour if you don't hang about. It takes a bit longer coming back up those cliffs, though.'

'I know, I found a beautiful little beach this morning.'

'Shh, don't tell the tourists,' Mairi said, and Nessa giggled. That response seemed to be a standing joke with the villagers.

'A lady in the charity shop said the same thing.'

'Catrin Williams?'

'Yes.'

'Nice girl. I've known her since she was a babe in arms, too.'

'I take it you've lived here all your life?'

'I have, and I wouldn't want to live anywhere else. What about you? I've been told you come from Bristol, but there's a Welsh lilt in your voice.'

'I was born and bred in the Valleys, but I left to study nursing, got a job in Bristol Royal, and worked there ever since.'

'You didn't think to move back to your hometown?'

'There was nothing to move back for.'

'No family?'

'No.'

'What about a husband? Partner?'

'I was married once, a long time ago. It didn't work out.'

'I'm sorry. Do you have any children?'

'No, sadly not.'

Mairi reached across the little table and patted her hand. 'I'm being nosey, aren't I?'

'It's OK, I don't mind.' She did mind, though – not Mairi asking questions because Eleri at the cafe had asked questions too – but being on her own. She wouldn't have chosen this life; rather it had been thrust upon her. She'd had plenty of opportunities to meet fellas, but none of them had worked out. Nessa preferred to blame it on the demands of her job – it was better than believing no one wanted her enough to make a go of it. And it was too late now, of course. She was practically an old woman, so the most she could hope for was the love of good friends (when she made some – but she hoped she was making a start with Mairi) and her cat.

Mairi broke into a big smile. 'I've got a feeling we're going to be good friends, you and I, and it's such a relief to have someone as nice as you move in. I must admit, I was worried about who I might end up living next door to.'

'Do you see much of your other neighbours?'

'Not much. The couple on the other side are at work all day, the houses further down again are mostly holiday rentals.'

'What about George?'

'George is George.' Mairi pulled a face.

'Do you think he's lonely?' Nessa asked suddenly.

'He most definitely is.'

'How about if I ask him to join us for tea? Would you mind?'

'Of course not, but I very much doubt if he'll come.'

Nessa doubted it too, but there was no harm in asking, and at least he'd know someone cared; because she had an awful feeling it had been a very long time indeed since anyone gave a fig about George Nightingale.

Chapter 10

George

Today Nessa had gone out across the fields. Then had come back, and had gone out once more, returning with a couple of shopping bags. Then she'd gone out yet *again* – this time to bother old Mrs Edwards who lived two doors down. She'd been carrying the same tin she'd left on his doorstep yesterday evening and George took an educated guess as to what was in it.

His eyes slid towards the sitting room door as he thought about the last remaining piece of cake in the fridge. Unable to resist, he'd had a slice for breakfast. It knocked socks off his usual toast.

Nessa's constant to-ing and fro-ing was getting on his nerves, though – how was he supposed to get any work done when there was continual distraction from the woman next door?

Oh no! She'd now come out of Mrs Edwards' house and was traipsing up his own drive as if she owned the place, wearing a smile on her face and with a spring in her step.

Whatever it was she wanted, he wasn't interested.

The expected knock made him flinch, but he remained in his swivel chair, even though he was tempted to open the door and give her a piece of his mind. If he upset her, it would serve her right; she had no business bothering him, and if she kept on, he'd—

What? He could hardly call the police and make a complaint. He knew how those things worked – they'd pay him a visit and expect to come in. If watching those police shows with his father had taught George anything, it was that the police always wanted to come in. And he simply couldn't allow that to happen.

Therefore, he'd have to put up with nosey Nessa from next door until she got the hint and stopped bothering him. He didn't know how many failed attempts on her part to get him to interact with her it would take before she got the message he wasn't interested, but he had plenty of time on his hands and he was a patient man. He could wait her out. He guaranteed she'd get fed up before he did. Apart from his twice-daily trips into the village, he could hide behind his net curtains and his front door, safe in the knowledge she couldn't get to him. He would wait her out.

A second knock made him jump, and he put a hand on his chest to ease his racing heart.

He heard the letterbox rattle and he hoped she hadn't shoved another note through it, because if she had, she was wasting her time; he wasn't going to reply to it.

Her voice drifting down the hall and carrying into the sitting room, nearly made him cry out. For a worrying moment he'd thought she'd managed to get in, then he understood she was calling through the letterbox.

'Mr Nightingale? George? It's Nessa from next door. Are you in?'

She went quiet for a second and George hoped she would go away when he'd failed to answer her.

No such luck.

'George? If you are there, can you come to the door? I want to invite you to my house for tea this evening.'

He held his breath in case she might be able to hear him breathe.

'It's beef casserole and new potatoes. If you fancy joining us, we'll be eating at six. No need to bring anything, just yourself.'

Bring anything? What would he bring?

'Mairi is coming, too,' she added, 'so it won't just be me and you.'

With that, the letterbox rattled for a final time and he heard her footsteps on the path.

He breathed again, taking in gulps of air as though he'd been underwater for too long.

Mairi was going? God, that made it worse, not better. He'd successfully managed to avoid Mairi Edwards for years, apart from the occasional hello, which took place with averted eyes and a bland smile. Now and again she tried to engage him in conversation and he'd make sure he answered her pleasantly enough, but he never stopped to talk.

He never stopped to talk with anyone if he could help it.

The most conversation he had was with Sid, and that only occurred because the annoying man kept a hold of his paper or George's change until he'd received an answer to whatever unimportant question he'd asked. George rued the day when items were no longer simply rung up on the till but had to be handed over to be scanned first. It was one more level of interaction he could do without. There was a time when he'd have been able to grab a paper, drop the correct money on the counter and wave the newspaper in Sid's general direction. Then Sid had been able to ring up the sale in his own good time without George needing to be in the shop.

Not now though. These days Sid had to take the paper from him, scan it in and *talk* to him.

George could cope with the scanning bit; it was the talking bit he objected to.

He wondered what Nessa Millbrook and Mairi Edwards would find to talk about. Not him, he hoped. But even if his name did come up in conversation, there wouldn't be a great deal to say about him, if anything at all. He made sure of that.

He was still worrying about it later, when he was microwaving some spaghetti bolognese from a tin, and heard voices outside.

The noise was coming from the back of the house and he recognised the speakers.

Opening the kitchen window a crack, he listened hard.

Nessa and Mrs Edwards were in Nessa's garden, discussing her plans for the lawn. It certainly needed something doing to it because it was an overgrown mess. But that had suited George fine, because it meant no one used to go out there. Alys Griffiths had left it to its own devices, apart from a twice-yearly mow and trimming of the bushes which she had a workman do for her.

However, that was another thing to worry about now – the fact that Nessa would be out in her garden pottering around and she'd be able to see into his. No matter how careful he was, there was always the chance something might be seen. Take those stacked milk bottles, for instance; they appeared to have a mind of their own of late. George's stomach knotted at the thought of how rain might give the pile of plastic even less cohesion than it already had.

It was a major fear of his that his secret might be revealed, and he couldn't bear to think of anyone deriding him, or worse, pitying him for his tendency to hang onto things.

He knew deep down it wasn't right. But he didn't know what he could do about it. And what really troubled him, was that he didn't know whether he *wanted* to do anything or not about it. He was perfectly happy and fine as things were. He wasn't harming anyone and what he did inside his own four walls was up to him. And the very real fear at the back of his mind, was that all the things he'd worked so hard to preserve might be removed and thrown away. He couldn't bear it if that happened.

From when he was tiny, his father had drilled into him that it was wrong and immoral to be wasteful, that if you threw something away the odds were you'd need it shortly after you'd got rid of it. His father had been proved right time and time again; one of George's earliest memories was helping him search the garage for an old roll of barbed wire which he'd saved when John Porter's grandfather had put a new fence up in the field opposite. It was only a small length, George recalled, but it had been enough to repair the chicken coop three doors down and stop a fox from getting in. And John Porter's granddad had been about to throw it away.

George remembered the incident for two reasons: one was because he'd nicked his finger on the barbed wire and still had a tiny silvery scar on his pinkie finger to show for it; and another was that Mr Taylor (whose chickens they were), had given him a paper bag of nut crunch that Mrs Taylor had made that very morning, and the taste of the treat had remained with him to this day. Sticky and sweet, with chunks of nuts embedded in golden caramel, his mouth was watering just thinking about it—

What was that smell?

It was equally mouth-watering, but in a different way. Rich and aromatic, oniony, beefy… *oh*! Nessa from next door had said she was making beef casserole, so that must be what it was.

George wanted to slip out of his back door and investigate in the garden, but he couldn't get to it other than via the front door, up the side of the bungalow, and in through the gate. Usually it didn't bother him, but today it did. Although he guessed Nessa was probably going from her kitchen, which was at the rear of the cottage, to the garden and back again, he didn't want to risk being seen skulking down the side of his own house. So he stayed where he was, dull resentment building inside him.

The delicious aroma taunted him. It seemed to be saying that he too could be sitting down to a plate of homecooked food if only he'd answered her knock earlier.

He froze as a thought occurred to him.

He could pop around to Nessa's house right now. She'd said so. In less than five minutes he could be—

The microwave pinged, making him jump.

No! What was he thinking? He had a perfectly good meal in the spaghetti bolognese. He didn't need handouts from a neighbour. He wasn't some poor old soul like Mrs Edwards who was desperate for some company. Although, if he was being honest, what he *was* desperate for was a taste of that casserole, and he fervently wished Nessa Millbrook would leave a plate of it on his doorstep, the way she'd done with the cake.

George took the bolognese out of the microwave and blew on it. What a ridiculous thought – leaving a plate of casserole on his doorstep indeed! Anyone would think he was a stray cat which needed feeding.

Sullenly, he picked up his fork and began to eat.

However, the food tasted of salt and hopelessness, and he hurled both the half-full bowl and fork into the sink. The resulting clatter was far louder than he anticipated, the bowl splitting into three pieces and spraying gobbets of lumpy brown sauce everywhere.

George winced, the anger gone as swiftly as it had arrived.

What on earth had got into him?

He never became angry. Irritated and annoyed, certainly, but he never lost his temper.

This was all down to Nessa and her damned casserole! And now he'd have to purchase a new bowl. What a waste.

He hated waste.

But what he hated more was the way his heart lurched when Nessa's voice called, 'George? We heard a crash. Are you all right?'

Of course he wasn't all right.

'George?' Her voice came again.

There was nothing for it – he'd have to answer her or risk her knocking on his door. He stood on tiptoe and cranked the kitchen window open a little more. 'Fine,' he called through it.

'Are you sure?' Her voice was louder. He couldn't see her, but he assumed she must be standing right next to the garden fence.

'Perfectly,' he shouted.

'Would you like to join us? I was just about to dish up.'

'No.' He paused, then added. 'Thank you.'

'OK.' She sounded disappointed.

He was disappointed, too. Not only had his recklessness instigated a conversation which he hadn't wanted to have, but now he had to make another meal… and buy another bowl tomorrow.

However, despite his growling stomach, nothing in the cupboard or the fridge appealed, so he stalked out of the kitchen and went to bed despite it being so ridiculously early, leaving the mess to be cleaned up tomorrow.

At least if he was asleep he wouldn't have to deal with attractive interfering neighbours and tantalising smells.

Chapter 11

Nessa

'If you let me have the measurements, I can pick the curtains up from Catrin and start work on them today,' Gracie Stewart said down the phone the next morning.

Nessa hesitated. 'But I haven't paid for them.'

'It doesn't matter. Catrin won't mind if you pay her the next time you see her.'

'If you're sure…?'

'I am. Measure up now. I'll wait.'

Nessa took the phone with her into the kitchen, put it on the table and searched in a drawer for the tape measure.

'The width is fine,' she told Gracie a couple of minutes later, 'but I think I'll need the curtains shortened by about twenty-four inches.'

'That might leave enough fabric to make a couple of cushion covers, if you'd like?'

'Yes, please, if it's not too much trouble.'

'Not at all. I'll have them done for you by the end of the day.'

'Gosh, that's quick! Shall I fetch them from you? I can pop into the shop and pay Catrin what I owe her on the way.'

Gracie gave Nessa her address and they agreed a price. Nessa was delighted. The new curtains were going to look fab, although it might be an idea to give the kitchen a lick of paint before she hung them. She smiled as she thought of Mairi's kitchen. Nessa had thought hers was old-fashioned until she'd seen Mairi's. It suited the old lady though – Nessa couldn't imagine her in a shiny new one, although she could imagine herself in one of those. For the time being though, a fresh coat of paint on the walls, and perhaps some new cupboard doors, would give the room a more modern look. She couldn't afford a whole new kitchen just yet, so this was the next best thing. It was a shame, really, because there was nothing wrong with the cupboard doors she already had, but they were a deep pine colour and it made the kitchen appear gloomy and dark. She fancied white, to set off her new curtains. Oh, well…

It was going to be another nice day, and Nessa decided not to waste it. The paint could wait until tomorrow; today she intended to go for a walk because the weather forecast warned of rain and high winds by the end of the week, so it might be an ideal time to get the roller and brushes out then, when she'd be stuck indoors anyway.

Nessa followed the same path as yesterday and was soon on the beach again. As she dawdled along the high-tide mark of pebbles, seaweed and driftwood, she decided she could get used to this lifestyle – a leisurely breakfast followed by a morning stroll, lunch on her overgrown patio… she must do something about those bushes… It struck her anew how she could do that every day if she wanted to. She had no commitments, no work to go to, no one to answer to; it was liberating and scary at the same time.

She'd only been in Applewell for a few days and already she could see the benefit of having a structure to her days and her weeks. No wonder Eleri said people could set their watch by George's walks into the village – he liked routine. Most people liked some in their lives, and this was often shaped by the necessity of going to school or work, or organising their days around the needs of children, and so on.

And so it used to be for Nessa (work, that is, not the children part), but now that the sole claim on her time had been removed, she could see the days, weeks and months ahead stretching aimlessly in front of her. Redecorating her house would only keep her occupied for so long.

She could understand how the elderly, especially, became set in their ways, liking to do certain things at certain times, and woe betide if things didn't go to plan. She'd witnessed it so many times during the course of her career – elderly people who were brought in after a fall and who complained bitterly they were missing their favourite TV programme, or who needed an urgent operation yet still demanded they have a cup of tea at eleven o'clock, because that was the time they always had one.

George wasn't elderly though, she mused. Middle-aged, like her, but not old, and she wondered what he did with himself all day. Was he also retired? Did he work from home? Was he too ill to work? He appeared healthy enough from what she'd seen of him, but she knew from experience looks could often be deceptive.

The crash she'd heard yesterday evening, as she was just about to go indoors and dish up their meal, played on her mind. It was probably nothing and George himself had said he was fine, but there was something nagging at her. Something she couldn't put her finger on.

It might be none of her business – actually, it most definitely *wasn't* any of her business – but she intended to find out. After all, neighbours should look out for one another, and he'd been without an immediate neighbour for quite some time. He could always tell her to sod off and mind her own business, and if he did, she'd respect that.

But she had a feeling he was shy, and not used to people caring about him. He reminded her a little of Sylvia. She'd been the same. When Nessa had first encountered her, the cat had been feral, despite her obvious pedigree. It pained Nessa that she would never know the cat's history (had she been abandoned, left to fend for herself?), but once she'd gained the animal's trust, Sylvia had settled into Nessa's life as though she'd always been in it. The cat, who had once been scared and distrustful, had blossomed into the most confident, opinionated and loving creature.

Was George like that?

Nessa recalled Mairi's potted history of the man's life, and her heart went out to him.

That he might neither need nor want her sympathy did occur to her, but she'd offer it anyway, and in the only way she knew how – by little acts of kindness. She'd tried yesterday evening with the invitation to tea, and she intended to continue in the same vein.

As she turned away from the beach to explore the little wooded valley with the stream running through it, she smiled to herself as she remembered the way she had gained Sylvia's trust was by feeding her. Nessa was mindful she shouldn't compare the gentleman next door to a half-starved moggie though, especially since he appeared far more together than Nessa herself was. When she'd seen George in the general store he'd been dressed very smartly indeed. Unlike Nessa, who hadn't worn anything but jeans, trainers and a T-shirt since she'd arrived in

Applewell. She hadn't done much with her hair either, and her face was make-up free.

She looked far scruffier than George, and more in need of some attention. He clearly didn't need anyone to iron his shirts for him or do his washing (not that she was offering) because she'd seen a few items of clothing fluttering on the line. Nessa still needed to have her washing machine plumbed in.

With that in mind, along with the rest of the jobs she yet had to do, Nessa climbed up the wooded path which wove its way up the valley through the trees, until she eventually came out on the opposite side of the village to Oak Lane.

Perfect. As she'd hoped yesterday, she could combine this new walk with a trip to the shops if she needed anything. And while she was here, she'd pay Catrin for the curtains, and pop into Pins to Elephants for some paint. The sooner she began redecorating, the sooner she'd finish, and then she'd be able to relax.

'What are you making this time?' The man behind the counter in Pins to Elephants was chatting to a woman making a purchase, as Nessa waited to be served.

She'd chosen a very soft shade of lavender paint to complement the deeper lavender shade in the curtains. It was one of those 'barely there' colours and she hoped it would work a treat. It was a long time since she'd done any decorating and she'd never had a particularly good eye for it.

'I found a couple of pallets the other day, and thought I'd have a go at making myself a workbench for the shed. I need a new saw before I begin, though.'

Nessa raised her eyebrows in surprise at the woman's abilities. Nessa was reluctant to put up a shelf, never mind attempting to make furniture from scratch.

When it was her turn to be served, she asked the man if he knew of anyone who would install new cupboard doors.

'You should take a leaf out of our Lottie's book,' the man laughed. 'She don't believe in buying anything new. She'd slap a new coat of paint on the doors she's already got.'

'She would?'

'Aye.' He peered at her. 'You've bought Alys Griffiths' old place, haven't you?'

'I think the whole village must know who I am.' She stuck out her hand. 'Nessa Millbrook.'

He shook it. 'Tony Hughes. How are you settling in?'

'Getting there,' she replied as she paid for the paint. 'It'll be a while yet; I've got a heap of painting to do, but at least the house is straight. I couldn't rest until I'd unpacked everything and put it away. I'm a bit of a neat freak.'

'You're living next door to the wrong person, then,' Tony muttered, before looking down, a hint of red creeping up his neck.

'I'm sorry, I don't follow you?'

'Never mind. How do you like the village?'

Tony's change of subject was glaringly obvious, but Nessa went with it, describing her walk this morning and telling him how friendly and welcoming everyone had been so far.

'Is Mairi back from her daughter's yet?' he asked.

'She came back yesterday afternoon,' she told him and although Nessa chatted about Mairi, she continued to wonder what he'd meant by his odd remark about her neighbours. Mairi's cottage was tidy enough, even if it was behind-the-times. It was perfect just the way it was from what she'd seen of it, and Nessa particularly loved the butler sink. The kitchen would be cosy and snug in the winter with the range to keep it warm, and she thought that having the armchairs in there was a great idea. To sit in one of them on a cold winter afternoon with a cup of tea and a book would be divine.

She was still mulling over the strange turn in the conversation as she cleaned the walls of her kitchen down later that afternoon in preparation for painting the next day. It was only when she was halfway up a ladder, trying to reach a stubborn corner, that she noticed George in his garden fetching his washing in, and she realised Tony mightn't have been referring to Mairi at all.

Chapter 12

Nessa

The good weather had been replaced by rain, winds and lowering clouds by the time Nessa had put the second coat of paint on the kitchen walls and declared the task complete. She'd hung the curtains too and the room looked brighter and fresher as a result of her hard work.

The only fly in the ointment was the old units, but she was resigned to having to live with them until she could afford to replace the doors.

She'd mentioned them to Gracie when she had picked up the curtains and cushion covers from the seamstress. Gracie had also suggested that Nessa should paint over the ones she already had.

Gracie, Nessa had discovered, was a pretty woman in her early thirties who lived for sewing. Nessa had been shown into a workroom at the front of Gracie's terraced house, and she'd never seen so much fabric in all her life.

'I can't thank you enough for altering these,' Nessa had said when Grace handed her the curtains, and she had to admit that now they were hung, the repurposed curtains looked perfect. She'd just picked some Spanish bluebells from her overgrown garden, and they now sat in a vase on the table, the vibrant purple-blue petals contrasting with the green of their leaves and stems, picking up the same colours in the fabric.

The room was starting to come together and Nessa was mightily pleased with what she'd achieved so far. But no matter how pleased she was with her kitchen, after being cooped up in her house for the past three days she was itching to get outside.

She had sturdy boots and a waterproof coat, and she had promised herself a walk along the clifftops when the weather was wild and windy, so she donned both, added a knitted hat to her ensemble and was ready to go.

For once Sylvia let her leave without a murmur, having taken one look at the rain and deciding her mistress was mad to venture out in it. Instead, the cat sat in her customary place on the bedroom windowsill and watched Nessa as she strode across the field, the grass sodden underfoot and the ground squelchy with mud.

Soon Nessa's boots were caked in it, but at least the rain had eased, although the wind continued to whip around her head and through the branches of the bushes and small trees which formed the hedges.

It was exhilarating, and when she arrived at the coastal path the updraft as the wind tore up the cliff and blasted her in the face took her breath away. She didn't dare risk moving off the path to peer over the edge of the cliff as it was dangerous enough without the wild weather, but she only had to look along the coastline to see the enormous waves rolling in and slamming against the rocks. The sound of the sea, combined with the wind howling around her ears and the calls of the seabirds which were being buffeted high above, transformed the previously peaceful scene into a cacophony of sound.

Nessa squealed with delight. This was nature in the raw, and the sheer wild beauty of it made her feel so alive that she held her arms out to her sides and leant forward ever so slightly to let the wind take some of her weight. She was so happy, she was almost dancing with joy as she trotted towards the place where the path diverged to take her down to the sheltered cove.

As soon as she left the clifftop, the wind dropped dramatically and the howl became nothing more than a gust. The sound of the waves didn't diminish though, and the roar followed her as she began the steep descent.

Now that she was no longer in danger of having her head blown off, Nessa removed her hat to let the wind snap at her hair and she felt droplets of seawater coat her face. When she licked her lips, she tasted salt and grinned. This was fun – there was nothing like a bracing walk along the coast to blow away the cobwebs, especially when there wasn't another soul around—

Damn it! She'd only taken a few steps down the incline when she realised someone was on the beach.

She'd failed to notice the figure at first because it was standing so motionless that her eyes had skimmed over it. But when it moved, it had caught her eye, a dark figure on the strip of light sand.

It was a man, she thought, although she couldn't be certain.

He was currently walking slowly across the beach, away from her, his hands in his pockets, shoulders hunched. Then he stopped, turned to face the sea and stood there. Now she could see his profile, she realised he was definitely a man. Nessa thought there was something of the Romantics about him, something which reminded her of

Lord Byron in solitary isolation on that wild and lonely beach.

She debated whether to carry on down to the cove or not, and decided she would. If he was still there when she reached level ground, she'd find a rock to perch on and wait for him to leave. She'd hoped to have the beach to herself today. She loved people, but she wanted to be alone in this wild place and think about what she should do with the rest of her life. There was no rush, she had all the time in the world, but she felt she needed some space in which to consider her options, and if she'd stayed in the cottage she would have found things which needed her attention, and another day would have slipped through her fingers. She might be officially retired, but fifty-five was far too young to throw in life's towel. A different direction was what she needed; something to keep her mind ticking over and provide some structure to the week would be a good idea.

Nessa was so lost in her own thoughts, she didn't realise she'd almost come to a standstill. Her steps had become slower and slower until she was dawdling along the path and as she glanced down to see how far she had left to go, she noticed the man again. For a second she'd forgotten he was there and she frowned because he didn't look like he was planning to leave anytime soon. He clearly hadn't noticed her. He was standing in the same spot, in the same position, and she might have thought he was intending to remain there until the tide came fully in and he was swamped. But then he did something she hadn't been expecting.

Just as she had done a few minutes ago up on the clifftop, he held his arms out at right-angles to his body, and she continued to watch curiously.

Suddenly he took off, racing down the beach, swooping and gliding, zigzagging across the sand. Nessa gasped – he looked exactly like a little boy pretending to be an aeroplane. And when he reached the end of the beach, he turned and came hurtling back in her direction. The faint sound of a human pretending to be a plane, complete with strafing noises from imaginary guns, drifted across the sand.

But her surprise turned to incredulity when she realised who it was.

The man was none other than her neighbour, George.

No wonder she hadn't recognised him straight away. He looked so different. Gone were the smart trousers, jacket, shirt and tie, and in their place was a pair of jeans, boots and an anorak. He appeared different, less severe, less precise. In fact, he looked playful and exuberant – neither words that she would have associated with her standoffish uptight neighbour.

Nessa continued to stare at him as his mood sobered, and he drew to a halt.

He was closer now and she could see his face clearly. His hair was tousled, his skin glowed from the exercise and the fresh air, as he again stopped and turned to stare out to sea, in profile once more.

This time he was less Byronic and more like Rochester or Heathcliff, dark and brooding, with the faintest hint of danger – and a little shiver ran through her. If she didn't know he was George from next door, she'd think he was someone else entirely; someone rather attractive. Someone whose good looks had been hiding behind a stiff exterior and a tendency to dress like a banker in a 1930s movie.

Oh hell. He shifted slightly as though he felt he was being watched, and then he spotted her. Their eyes met and held.

They stared at each other for long seconds.

Nessa felt as though he was drawing her in, that she was falling, and with a curse she looked away. When she plucked up the courage to look again, it was to find him still staring at her. Self-consciously, she waved at him.

George didn't wave back.

Instead, he hunched his shoulders, put his head down and trudged up the beach towards the little valley leading to the village, until he was quickly lost from view, leaving Nessa wondering if she'd imagined the whole thing.

But there was one thing she was certain she hadn't imagined, and that was the surge of attraction she'd felt towards him.

Chapter 13

George

It felt strange to be out. This wasn't his predictable twice-daily walk into the village. This felt like unexplored territory, and it made no difference that once, a long time ago, he'd practically lived in this cove.

Other people, other children had come here – of course they did, but he'd nearly always heard them coming and had then slipped back up the narrow track which led to the cliffs and the path home. Everyone else from the village used the other path, the one from the bottom end of the village, because it was closer to the centre of Applewell, and less steep as well as being more direct. The route from his house to the cove had been his own private one. Or so he liked to pretend.

These days dog walkers frequented it, but when he was a child people never seemed to walk dogs. Not like they did now. Back then the animals roamed free, sent out in the morning along with the kids and allowed back home in the evening, so in essence they exercised themselves.

How things had changed since he was young, George mused as he had picked his way carefully down the track, scared he might lose his footing on the uneven and muddy surface. And he wasn't all that old, either. Not like Mrs

Edwards, who was in her eighties. She'd seen far greater changes than he had.

He had managed to get to the bottom without incident, his knees and ankles aching with the unaccustomed strenuous exercise, and he had then clambered unsteadily over several rocks before stepping onto the firm sand.

My God, he'd forgotten how much he used to enjoy coming here, especially on days like this when he would not see a soul.

George took a deep breath of the spray-laden air, the distinctive smell of seaweed and the ocean filling his nose, propelling him instantly back to his childhood. There had been good days dotted amongst the bad, enough of the good ones to keep him going, and as he'd grown older the good ones had become more frequent. Then he'd stopped coming here – which was ironic considering this was the place where the majority of those good times had occurred. He used to spend hours dipping in and out of the rock pools, he'd found hidden caves only visible at low tide, and had explored them with little regard to the danger. He'd raced sticks down the stream in the valley, made infinitely more fun after a stiff rainfall, and he'd built dens in the undergrowth which blanketed the valley's sides.

As he walked slowly now on the beach, George felt the give of sand under the soles of the old boots he'd found in the charity shop yesterday. It had grieved him to buy them when there were several pairs in the bungalow, if only he could reach them.

There was that feeling again, that things were getting away from him. He had experienced it most acutely yesterday when he'd made the decision to go where his younger self had trodden, and go on the walk he had watched Nessa take. Until, that is, he was unable to reach any suitable attire. Reach, not find, because he hadn't *lost* his old boots. He knew precisely where they were – in his wardrobe. But there were too many things in the way, and he didn't have the courage to try moving anything. The effort wasn't worth it. And that was when he'd felt his world tilting again, because what was the point of keeping things he knew would come in handy someday, when he had to go out and buy new anyway?

The waves weren't as violent in the cove, most of their power having been spent on the rocks guarding the small headlands either side, but they rolled in relentlessly, one after another, after another. He could see them forming when they were far out in the open water, swelling and rising, flecked with white where the wind whipped at their crests, speeding towards him with frothy determination to rise up and curl over. For the briefest of moments, they hung in perfect symmetry before gravity won and they crashed against the shore, their cohesion smashed by the deceitful sand.

Soft, pale gold sand. Sifting through one's fingers like the finest icing sugar, yet powerful enough to tear waves apart, sand fascinated him, especially that which lay below the high tide mark. When dry it was benign, playful, comforting even, as it oozed through toes, yet when wet it was as hard as concrete.

He suddenly thought about sandcastles. Maybe he'd build a sandcastle one day, like he'd done so many times when he'd been a child.

Not today though.

Today he wanted to fly.

And with that, he spread his arms wide and hurtled across the beach at full speed, running parallel to the advancing waves, twisting and turning. As he ran, a long-forgotten memory of watching old Second World War films with his father skittered into his head, and he recalled how he'd pretended to be a Spitfire. Before he knew it, he was making tat-tat-tat noises and shooting enemy planes out of the sky.

Too unfit to keep his antics up for long, George came to a gasping halt at the near end of the beach, where the little path led steeply upwards, emerging onto the clifftops above. Home lay that way, but he wasn't ready to go back yet. This brief taste of the freedom he'd allowed himself was nowhere near enough. He was greedy, he wanted more.

Catching his breath, he stared out to sea once more, marvelling at the colours nature had painted – so many shades of grey, and each one different and distinct. It looked like a monochrome painting, a true watercolour of sea, wet rocks and rain-drenched sky – and he wished he had the ability to capture it in paint, although he believed nothing manmade would ever do it justice.

Abruptly he felt a prickling down the back of his neck, some sixth sense of being observed, which made him look to his right and up at the cliff he had recently descended. It was then he saw Nessa.

She was motionless, watching him.

He wondered what she'd seen, what she was still seeing as she stared at him, a look of intense concentration on her face.

He stared back. He wanted to look away, but before he could find the strength, she'd found enough for both of them and the contact was broken.

As was his mood.

It was time he returned, but she was up there blocking his path, so George had no choice other than to retreat up the valley.

He didn't move, though, and continued to stare at her until her gaze returned to his.

He might have stood there all day, but then she waved to him.

It was a small thing, that wave, an inconsequential gesture of acknowledgement, perhaps even friendship, but it was enough to spur him on, and he whirled around, his back to the sea, and hurried up the beach.

He didn't look back.

He didn't want to acknowledge her and he certainly didn't want her friendship. Friends had expectations and demands. And he didn't want anyone expecting anything from him, and neither did he want to be needed; he'd had enough of that to last him a lifetime. He simply wanted to be left alone. He was happy alone doing his own thing, minding his own business.

A line of Shakespeare flashed into his head cutting through his thoughts, 'the lady doth protest too much, methinks', but his mind swapped the word 'lady' for 'gentleman', and he wondered if it was true. Was he protesting too much?

Of course he wasn't.

But if that was the case, why was he starting to feel as if everything was unravelling? The freedom he'd briefly experienced when he'd diverged from his usual morning route to the village and had cut across John Porter's field instead, was unsettling. And he couldn't help feeling some reluctance at the thought of returning to the bungalow.

He called it 'the bungalow', not 'home'.

The distinction was telling. It was his home, it always had been up until he found a job in Liverpool, but then gradually it had become his 'parents' house'. Even when he'd moved back in after the death of his mother and it truly was his home, George still felt as though it belonged to his father and he was merely visiting.

It was odd to realise he still thought of it in that way, despite him being its sole occupant and having inherited it. His name was on the deeds. It was his house.

But it wasn't his *home*.

He had no idea where that was.

The bungalow was more like a tomb, and he feared it might become one in reality one day; because what if one of the stacks of books in his living room toppled into another, then a third, and the whole lot came down and buried him? He could die and no one would know.

Sadness cloaked him. That his life had come to this was heartbreaking, but he could see no way out. His things were his things. He couldn't imagine getting rid of them. Who would take them? He couldn't throw them away because that would go against everything his father had instilled in him. And his father was right. George never wasted anything, and therefore he never wanted for anything – he pushed aside the memory of rooting around in the charity shop for today's outfit of boots and jeans. It had been an anomaly and it wouldn't happen again. And later on this afternoon he would return said boots to the charity shop from whence they came.

Yet even as he was planning on doing it, George knew he wouldn't. He knew he'd never make the effort to reach his own sturdy footwear marooned in his wardrobe. He knew the ones he was currently wearing would end up being kept, and he grew cross at the thought.

As he stomped up the hill, he knew who was to blame for him being so out of sorts this past week – his new neighbour. Nessa was a busybody, and she hadn't stopped bothering him since she'd moved in, baking him a cake when he didn't want it, inviting him to supper when he didn't want to be invited, making him envy her freedom to come and go.

And where had it got him? Puffing and panting his way up a soggy valley on a wet and windy morning, that's where, when he should have been fetching his newspaper and be on his way home.

She'd done nothing but irritate him and he simply didn't know how long he'd be able to carry on like this. He'd even heard her singing yesterday, warbling away to some rubbish on Radio Two. She'd sounded *happy*.

Which was why he'd made the rash decision to take a journey not travelled for a very long time, and look where he'd ended up – on a windswept beach, with spray on his face, salt on his lips and emptiness in his heart.

And then he'd seen her, perched on the path above him and he'd wondered if she'd followed him. Why was she haunting him? Spying on him like this?

He knew he was being unreasonable to think like that, but he couldn't seem to shift the idea that her continuing to live in the cottage next door was going to cause him more problems than her presence had already caused. Change was afoot, he could sense it.

But the question at the forefront of his mind was, would the coming change destroy him or save him? Right now, he felt his life could go either way.

Chapter 14

Nessa

That blimmin' cat was going to add yet more grey hairs to Nessa's already salt-and-peppered locks. The little minx had gone missing again. Nessa's efforts to deliberately keep Sylvia in for the first few days after they'd moved in, to try to get her accustomed to the house and her new territory, had clearly been in vain.

She understood that she was probably being overcautious considering Sylvia had escaped at least once already and had found her own way back easily enough. But Nessa wasn't prepared to take any chances. She had just started letting her out, when the weather had taken a turn for the worse, and Sylvia hadn't been very keen to go out when it had been blowing a gale outside and lashing it down. She had been content to sit on the windowsill and chase raindrops down the glass, but this morning Nessa had woken to clear skies and sunshine. With it being calm and serene outside, the cat had been more than happy to dart through the open kitchen door and had slipped like a shadow into the undergrowth.

Sylvia never went far, though, and she nearly always came running when Nessa rattled her bowl and called out. However, it was now early evening and Nessa had been calling and calling, and Sylvia hadn't shown. Nessa was starting to get worried.

She'd seen Sylvia nip over the fence separating her house from George's bungalow earlier in the day, and she wondered if the cat had found her way into his house and couldn't manage to get back out again.

'Sylvia,' she called again and rattled the biscuits in the cat's bowl. Then she listened intently for the sound of an answering chirp, but all she could hear was the drone of a tractor in the distance, the closer bark of a dog and the noisy chatter of a pair of sparrows who were telling her off for disturbing them.

Should she knock on George's front door and ask him to check his outbuildings? She hadn't seen much of him since their encounter in the cove the other day – although she had spotted him hurrying down the road yesterday morning, presumably to fetch his paper. She's only seen him from the back as she was straightening the curtains in the living room after dusting the windowsill, so she hadn't had the opportunity to wave to him. She's also caught a glimpse of him on the path running down the side of his house, but again he'd had his back to her then, picking up a fallen branch from somewhere or another that the storm had left for him.

'Sylvia! Come on, sweetie! Dinner!' she called, glancing across at the bungalow.

Still nothing.

She'd wait a few more minutes and try calling the cat one more time, but then she'd have no choice but to pop to George's house.

A final call and a rattle, and Nessa gave in. It was time to pay George a visit.

But before she did, she checked her appearance in the hall mirror. Then, as this wasn't something she usually did before leaving the house, she wondered why she'd done so now. Irritated with herself, she walked away without taking a good look – she'd have to trust that her hair didn't look like a birds' nest or that she wasn't wearing some of her lunch down her top.

Nessa lifted her chin, and marched out of her house and up to George's front door. Her knock was firm and determined, three short loud raps with her knuckles.

Then she waited.

No answer.

It didn't come as a surprise; she hadn't expected one.

However, footsteps behind her were a surprise and she spun around to find George walking up his path, not looking pleased to see her on his doorstep.

She, though, was delighted to see him, and she tried to scrutinise him without appearing to be scouring him from head to foot.

He looked considerably different from the other day on the beach. For one thing, he had far more formal attire on, as he was wearing a suit and a tie, with a pair of well-polished black shoes on his feet.

On closer inspection, as he approached his own door, she noticed the suit had seen better days, and was that a frayed edge on the collar of his shirt?

His hair was neatly combed, though, and he was clean-shaven. He wasn't quite the tortured Romantic poet she'd portrayed him to be on the beach, but she had to admit he was incredibly attractive for a middle-aged man. He was no Daniel Craig, but then again, who was?

To her astonishment a tremor ran through her, but she couldn't tell whether it was because he was glowering at her or because she fancied the socks off him. Who'd have thought it? Astounded at her reaction to her curmudgeonly neighbour, she resisted an impulse to give him a wave, the way she'd done from her clifftop perch, and sent him a bright smile instead.

'Hi,' she followed up with, equally brightly.

He continued to glower. 'Can I help you?'

'Um, yes, I'm looking for my cat.'

George's frown intensified. 'Were you expecting to find it at my front door?' he asked in a suspicious tone, as if looking for her cat was an excuse, and in reality she was casing the joint.

'Not exactly. But Sylvia might be inside, maybe?'

'I hardly think so.'

'Do you mind taking a look? Cats are quite ingenious at getting into places.'

His eyes widened, and she saw they were a most attractive shade of hazel with golden flecks in them. The crow's feet around them lessened a little as he stopped scowling quite so much, but they didn't disappear completely – much like her own, which were a permanent feature along with the small line dissecting her brow between her eyebrows. She saw that George had two lines, probably caused by that impressive frown of his.

'Now?' he demanded, and his voice carried as much incredulity as if she had asked him to dance a waltz whilst wearing a chicken outfit.

'If you don't mind.' She could tell by the way his jaw hardened and the huffed sigh that he did mind.

'If you'll be kind enough to take a step back and let me get to my door…?'

'Oh, silly me, of course. Sorry.' Nessa moved out of the way.

Not far enough, it seemed, as George continued to stare at her. She retreated a little further.

His lips tightened but he stepped forward to unlock his front door.

Then he did something rather curious. Instead of opening it and walking through it like a normal person, he eased it open a crack and slipped through, denying her even the smallest glimpse of what lay beyond. Nessa had been poised to have a quick peek, but didn't think it could be anything special – the house was a bungalow at the end of a lane in a small Welsh village, for goodness' sake – but his odd behaviour sent her imagination into overdrive. What was he hiding in there? Was the inside of his bungalow a gilded palace, full of unseen treasures? Or did he have a *Fifty Shades of Grey* thing going on? No wonder Eleri from the cafe and Tony from Pins to Elephants had alluded to some weirdness on George's part.

The door closed with a firm snick and Nessa stood there, wondering what she should do. Was George looking for Sylvia and would be back out in a minute, or was he going about his normal business and had forgotten she was still waiting on his driveway?

Nessa shuffled from foot to foot, craning her neck to see in the glass of the door, whilst trying not to appear nosey. She'd give him a minute, then she'd knock again.

One minute passed, then two, before she gave in and knocked.

It took a while, but George finally came to the door.

And when he did, his behaviour was equally as odd as it had been a few minutes ago. The door opened a smidgeon, and one eye and half a face came into view. She tried to see past him, but he was effectively blocking her view.

'Have you found her?' she asked.

'No.'

'Did you actually look?'

'Yes.'

'Oh. Right. OK. I'll… um… be off then.'

No response.

'If you do happen to see her, could you let me know?' she added.

He gave a brief nod and she had to be contented with that. Nessa turned around and was about to walk away, when she stopped.

'Can I ask you something?' she said, then ploughed on before George had a chance to respond. 'Do you by any chance write poetry?'

There was that widening of his eyes again. 'No.'

Nessa shrugged. 'You reminded me of… Never mind.' An embarrassed laugh escaped her and she quickly headed down the drive before she could say anything else. What on earth had she been thinking of – of course he didn't write poetry! She'd bet her right arm he didn't read it either. How silly of her to imagine him as a tortured poet when the poor man had only been out for a walk on the beach.

Nessa blamed it on the weather. It had been wild and romantic, and she'd allowed her imagination to run away with her. She was doing the same when it came to the inside of George's bungalow. It was probably quite ordinary and, now that she'd stopped being ridiculous, she imagined it having 1970s décor and a faint smell of boiled cabbage. No wonder he wasn't too keen on people seeing inside, if that was the case.

When she reached the bottom of his drive and turned onto the pavement, she risked a glance at his front door.

It was closed, but she had the feeling he was watching her from inside – probably to make sure she didn't show up on his doorstep asking more strange questions, she thought.

Keen to see a friendly face, Nessa headed for Mairi's cottage. Sylvia was just as likely to have gone in there as she was to have sneaked into George's house. It was getting late and Nessa was becoming increasingly concerned. Sylvia was more of an indoor than an outdoor cat and she wasn't overly enamoured with being outside after dark; she liked a comfy sofa and a warm radiator, and she also liked to sleep in Nessa's bed, curled up beside her mistress. She was also a greedy cat, despite her lithe slimness, and it was unlike her not to come running when the rattle of her biscuits promised there would be a chance of food.

Nessa rang Mairi's doorbell, then clasped her hands together, praying nothing untoward had happened to the little feline. She didn't think she could bear it.

She heard Mairi's shuffled footsteps, then the door opened. As soon as the gap was wide enough, a cream and soot figure shot out through the gap, nearly toppling Mairi over. She put a hand out to the wall to steady herself.

'Are you OK?' Nessa asked, stepping forward to take the old lady by the elbow.

'I'm fine. Surprised, that's all. Was that your cat?!'

'Yes, I'm so sorry. I've been looking for her and I guessed she might have got herself shut inside somewhere.'

The cat was now sitting in the middle of the lawn, one leg defiantly raised, grooming herself without a care in the world.

Nessa scolded her. 'I've been worried about you. What were you doing in Mairi's house? And you nearly knocked her over.'

Sylvia continued to ignore her.

'Come in,' Mairi urged. 'I was about to have a cup of tea.'

'I don't want to be any bother, but thank you. Let me round Sylvia up and I'll be right with you.' Nessa scooped the cat up, marched along the pavement and up her own drive. As she did so, she couldn't help glancing at the bungalow next door. George probably wasn't looking, but she held the cat up for him to see she'd found her, just in case he did happen to be looking out of his window at that very moment. Maybe she'd pop around later to let him know she'd found her errant moggie.

With that, she shoved the cat through the front door and closed it firmly, before she returned to Mairi's for a nerve-calming cup of tea.

'She must have got in when I was fetching my washing in,' Mairi said when Nessa had let herself in and had made her way into the kitchen. The old woman was pouring boiling water into a teapot. 'Or it might have been when I put some rubbish in the bin.'

'If she comes in again and you notice her, shoo her back out. And whatever you do, don't feed her, else you'll never get rid of her,' Nessa warned. 'I'm sorry she bothered you.'

'Don't be, I rather like cats.'

'I don't think my other neighbour does,' Nessa pointed out. 'I don't think he likes me, either. And here I was, hoping we could be friends. Of sorts.'

'He keeps himself to himself. Always has done. It can't have been easy for him, growing up. His parents were late having him and they mollycoddled him. Too much, if you ask me. It didn't help that he was a swotty little thing, and children can be so cruel. Here you go,' She handed Nessa a cup and saucer.

'Thank you.' She took a sip of her tea. 'I saw him in the cove the other day, when we had that awful weather. He was running up and down the beach, like a little boy.'

Mairi spluttered and nearly spilt her drink. 'He was doing *what*?' she asked, when she'd caught her breath. 'You must have been mistaken. George only ever goes into the village.'

Nessa grinned, enjoying Mairi's disbelief. 'It was definitely George, although I must admit I didn't recognise him at first.'

'I'm not surprised, if he was behaving in that manner. Are you sure it was him?'

'Positive. He looked different though. I've only ever seen him dressed as if he was going to the office, but that day he was wearing jeans. That wasn't it, though. He looked… I don't know… younger? More carefree?' Nessa decided not to share her Heathcliff/tortured-poet imaginings.

Mairi snorted and shook her head. 'He was born old, that one. He has always looked like he's got the weight of the world on his shoulders.'

'Tony, in Pins to Elephants, said something strange to me the other day – he was asking me how I'd settled in, and I said I'd got loads of painting to do but at least I'd unpacked everything, which was a relief because I'm a bit of a neat freak, and he muttered that I was living next door to the wrong person. What do you think he meant by that?'

Mairi shrugged. 'It's rumoured that George is a hoarder. Don't get me wrong – I don't know for certain and his garden is always as neat as a pin – but Alys, who owned your cottage before you bought it, used to say he never put any bins out, apart from the little one for the food waste.'

Nessa frowned. 'Not putting bins out isn't sufficient evidence to conclude he's a hoarder.' She slapped a hand to her forehead. 'Darn it, that reminds me – I think I've missed bin-collection day.'

'You haven't missed it; they come tomorrow.'

'Thank goodness for that! I've got *a lot* of boxes to get rid of. Will they take them, do you think?' Nessa had already removed the packing tape and folded them up. She'd put them in her shed, but she didn't want to leave them there to rot, and they also took up too much space. She had half a tonne of newspapers she'd wrapped her china and other breakable things in, which needed to go, too.

'I'm sure they will. I don't get many boxes to throw out, but when I do, I put them next to the paper and cardboard bin and they take them.'

'This recycling business is complicated,' Nessa observed. 'I don't want to get on the wrong side of the bin men, or cause them any problems.'

'You're a good girl,' Mairi said with a gentle smile, and Nessa smiled back.

She was hardly a girl, but she was about thirty years younger than Mairi, so she supposed to the old lady, she might very well be.

Nessa was still smiling to herself when she returned to her own house a short while later, intending to take the various recycling boxes down to the end of the drive in anticipation of them being emptied tomorrow. She'd feed Sylvia first though, because the cat was rubbing up against her legs, weaving in and out, and meowing loudly.

'You could have had your tea earlier if you hadn't been so naughty,' Nessa scolded her as she opened a pouch of evil-smelling cat food and forked it into a bowl.

Sylvia yowled louder until Nessa put it on the floor and the cat devoured it as though she hadn't been fed for a week, although Nessa clearly recalled the cat enjoying a breakfast of similar proportions earlier on in the day.

She waited for Sylvia to finish eating, then picked up the dish and put it next to the draining board. Not really expecting a thank you, Nessa still laughed as she watched her furry friend stalk off and jump onto the sofa to wash her face.

'You're welcome,' Nessa said, sardonically, then went to complete her chores.

With her assorted bins now placed at the end of the drive, Nessa saw Mairi hadn't put hers out yet, so she strolled around to Mairi's and offered to take hers down the drive.

'Thank you, dear, that's very kind of you,' the old lady said, gratefully.

'It's no bother – I can do this every week, if you like?'

'That would be wonderful. I don't have a lot of rubbish, but it can still be a struggle sometimes, if my hips are playing up.'

Nessa gave the woman a swift peck on the cheek. Poor love, it must be hard having one's family live so far away, and she was happy to give Mairi any assistance she could.

As she was walking back to her own property, Nessa checked the end of George's drive. The only thing on the pavement was the lockable green caddy for food waste. Mairi was right. How strange.

Tony, Mairi and the rest of the people in Applewell must have got the wrong end of the stick, though, because

George didn't look like a hoarder. Not that hoarders had a particular *look*, she reminded herself, but then she knew from catching a couple of episodes of *Britain's Biggest Hoarders* on TV it wasn't always possible to tell from the outside of a house whether people were hoarders or not. The houses tended to look perfectly neat and tidy from the outside, as did the people who lived in them.

Just as she was about to go into her cottage and settle down for the evening, she saw George's net curtain twitch, and she gave him a wave.

There was no response.

Then again, she hadn't expected to receive one.

Well, if neither waving nor invitations to tea worked, maybe another cake would?

If he hadn't thrown the last one in the bin…

But there must be a reason for the old saying that the way to a man's heart was via his stomach. Nessa had no intention of inveigling her way into George's heart, but she did want to be friends with him. Neighbours should get along and help one another, and she was determined to do just that, whether George wanted it or not!

Chapter 15

George

Seeing Nessa on his doorstep as he had returned from his walk had nearly given George a funny turn. His initial reaction had been visceral – his stomach had somersaulted and his heart had skipped a beat at the sight of her. Then common sense had kicked in and he shoved his irrational feelings away.

Hoping she hadn't seen anything untoward inside the house, as soon as Nessa had left, George had dashed into the living room and had watched her go to Mairi's house. A few minutes later, the cat had shot into view, haring down the path as though one of the hounds of hell was after it. George had then watched as the cat had suddenly sat down on Mairi's lawn, stuck a leg in the air and had begun licking its paw.

George, annoyingly, had a momentary pang when he realised Nessa's cat had preferred to hide out in Mairi Edwards' house rather than in his own. Mind you, he couldn't blame it. Mairi probably had a comfy armchair and titbits in her fridge.

Not content with the fussing and food it undoubtedly received at home, the feline had gone in search of fussing and food elsewhere. Cats, he decided, were as fickle and as unreliable as people.

Then he amended the thought, because he was wrong. People weren't fickle at all – they were very predictable. He'd discovered as much at quite a young age, when the horrible boys in school had teased and taunted him with the same words and in the same manner day after day.

Abruptly, Nessa had come into view again, dashed down Mairi's path and had pounced on the cat. She had scooped it up and marched towards her own front door, glancing in his direction once again.

He resisted the urge to hide behind the curtain.

Thinking the drama was all over for today, George had just stepped away from the glass when Nessa had reappeared once more, this time *sans* cat, and had walked up Mairi's path and into the old lady's house.

George had been unable to settle, and had taken the opportunity to put his food caddy out for the refuse collectors tomorrow. They usually arrived at around six in the morning and he didn't want to risk forgetting to put it out this evening. He always placed it at the end of his drive at this time, and he knew if he didn't do it now, he'd wake up in a cold sweat at three in the morning.

Nessa had remained in Mairi's house for thirty-three minutes.

When she emerged, she did her usual glance up at his bungalow, then she put her bins out.

He had thought she was done for the day, and he could finally relax, as she went back inside, but then suddenly here she was again, striding down her path, this time carrying an armload of flattened cardboard boxes, which she popped down next to one of her bins.

George eyed them with something akin to avarice.

He loved a good cardboard box; they were so handy. It was a shame to throw them out. Despite being told by the council that everything in the various recycling bins was recycled, George had his doubts, having read differing information in the media that there weren't enough recycling facilities to cope with even half the amount of stuff people threw out. He bet those boxes would end up in landfill.

Most things did.

He expected Nessa to go back indoors, but instead, she glanced down the road, went to Mairi's house *again* (Nessa may as well move in for all the time she spent there) and dragged the old lady's bins onto the pavement, too.

That was nice of her, George conceded.

He should have thought of offering to do that.

He'd noticed Mairi trundling her wheelie bins down her drive enough times, yet he hadn't stepped forward to help.

It wouldn't have hurt him. Once a fortnight, that was all. But reluctance to be drawn into any kind of relationship with his neighbours, no matter how fleeting, had held him back.

Now Nessa Millbrook was making him feel guilty about his lack of neighbourliness.

And why was she standing there now, at the bottom of her drive, studying his green food-waste caddy? It was the same as hers. The council provided them when they first brought in recycling to Applewell. Every household in the village had been given one.

What was so special about his, to make Nessa take undue interest in it?

He almost snarled when she gave him a little wave.

How on earth did she know he was watching her?

And that was another thing that made him feel bad – he was turning into a voyeur, always lurking behind his net curtains, and he didn't like this new aspect of himself in the slightest. What was it about Nessa Millbrook that made him act this way?

He should be able to ignore her.

After all, he successfully ignored everyone else up until now.

But somehow, she'd got under his skin, and he had no idea how to winkle her back out. He was fascinated by her; she seemed to have a weird hold on him, and she was hijacking his thoughts with increasing frequency. Not only that, but his body's reaction to her was like nothing he'd ever felt before.

It didn't help his confused state of mind either, to acknowledge to himself that as soon as it was dark, he knew he would sneak outside, grab Nessa's cardboard boxes and dash back inside with them.

How had his life got to this?

–

It was like that film everyone used to go on about, *Groundhog Day*, George thought later that evening – another day, same tin on his doorstep. With a plate on the top of it this time. Although why Nessa Millbrook should think he didn't have any plates of his own was beyond his comprehension. And he couldn't understand why it was covered in tin foil and there appeared to be something lumpy underneath the shiny covering.

George executed a similar move to the last time, as he opened his door a fraction, reached out with a stretched arm, his shoulder against the doorframe, hooked the tin, and pulled it inside. He was well aware his actions might look strange to anyone who might be watching, but he didn't care. The only person who could possibly be watching was that woman next door and he didn't give two hoots what she thought of him.

He took the tin into the kitchen and placed it on the tiny space in front of the microwave, then lifted the plate covered in foil from the top of it. When he unwrapped the foil (carefully, of course, to add it to his supplies) his mouth dropped open. He wasn't sure what he'd been expecting, but three decent-sized golden pasties wasn't it. He touched one of them. It was still warm and his finger depressed the pastry slightly.

He'd already eaten his evening meal of a reheated frozen shepherd's pie, but there was no harm in taking a bite of this. Just to try it.

Lifting the pasty to his nose, he sniffed it cautiously.

It smelt OK. More than OK, it smelt wonderful, and George wondered what variety it was. It looked like a Cornish one, but he was no expert when it came to pasties, therefore the only way to find out was to try one.

Gently, he nibbled the edge with his teeth, but all he got from the tiny bite were some flaky crumbs. They were delicious on their own, but he had to know what the filling was.

He took a larger bite this time, and his mouth was immediately filled with the exquisite flavours of vegetables. He identified carrots, onion, swede and potato, along with a hint of herbs, and maybe some garlic, as he wolfed it down, hardly chewing in his haste.

He dearly wanted another one, but that would be greedy, he thought, licking his lips and then his fingers, anxious to catch every last crumb.

Eyeing the remaining two savoury treats with longing, he transferred them onto his own plate, replaced the foil on top and popped the plate in the microwave without turning it on, to allow the pasties to cool down before he put them in the fridge later. Then he turned his attention to the tin and eased the lid off, his hands almost shaking with excitement. If this cake was anything like the last one…

A glorious aroma of chocolate and orange rose up from the inside of the tin. George's mouth instantly watered and he closed his eyes in bliss as he inhaled. Just like the last time, he was unable to resist, so he cut off a huge slice and bit into it.

Chocolate and orange – two of his favourite flavours.

The sponge was light and moist, and the buttercream melted on his tongue, filling his mouth with creamy loveliness.

Oh. My. Word.

He groaned in delight, trying to slow down and savour each mouthful, but it was hard not to stuff the whole lot in in one go.

He'd missed home baking. His mother used to bake all the time, and whenever he came back to Applewell as an adult she'd make a fuss by making him a cake, or some scones, or muffins. Shop-bought wasn't the same. And there was always a hearty freshly prepared meal waiting for him back then, too.

George was an adequate cook. Living by himself had meant, if he didn't want to starve, he either had to eat out (not his style to sit in a restaurant on his own), live off takeaways and frozen meals for one (much like he was doing now, except for the takeaway part) or learn to cook. He'd opted for the learn-to-cook option, and by the time he'd been forced to move back into his parents' house, he knew his way around an oven.

His problems with not cooking began even before George had lost his father. In the beginning he'd cooked – he'd had to, for his father's sake – but already there had been too many items stored in the kitchen to make it practicable or safe. And by the time his father had reached the point where he could only manage a couple of mouthfuls before he was finished, George had given up cooking altogether. Instead, he had learnt to survive on ready meals, cereal and toast. It was easier that way.

Finally full, George found a tin of his own – which wasn't hard to do as the whole side of one of the bedrooms was full of them – and popped the rest of the cake in there. He then rinsed out the one Nessa had provided and carefully wiped it dry.

He gazed at it for far longer than was strictly necessary.

Mind made up, he went back to the bedroom, and selected an old Roses tin. When he opened it to check the condition of its interior, there was a faint lingering smell of the chocolates it had once held many years ago. He then put the Roses tin on top of the container Nessa had left on his doorstep. After that, he washed and carefully dried her plate, went into the living room, sat at his desk and wrote her a note.

Thank you for the cake.

Keep the tin. You obviously need it.

He didn't mind donating one of his tins. It was going to a good home, especially since she appeared to only have the one – and if Nessa kept giving him gifts of baked goods then he would probably get it back anyway. He wouldn't take it around to her yet, though; he'd wait until much later on, when darkness had fallen and there was less chance of bumping into her. She had a tendency to pop in and out of her house like a jack-in-the-box. Actually, he had one of those somewhere… Perhaps he should give it to her? Maybe she would find it fun. If he could be certain she'd understand the reference and could be sure she'd treasure it, then he might. But he couldn't be sure she would do either of those things, so he decided to leave the old toy where it was. Someday he'd find a use for it. Someday he'd find a use for all of it.

Someday…

Chapter 16

Nessa

The plate, the tin and a note were waiting for her on the doorstep the following morning, as Nessa knew they would be. What she hadn't known was that an additional tin would also be sitting there.

When she turned her note over and read what George had written on the back of it, she smiled. It saved her buying another tin, she supposed. The new one she was holding in her hand was a proper tin, before chocolate manufacturers had moved from metal to plastic for their Christmas selections. George must have had it for quite some time, she surmised.

She read the note again, and chuckled quietly to herself. She wondered wryly whether George had donated the tin in the hope she would fill it.

Nessa nodded at George's bungalow. He might be watching; she suspected he did that a lot. Surprisingly, she didn't mind – he was lonely and his loneliness might be trapping him in his house as effectively as a bird was trapped in a cage. And if that truly was the case, she intended to do something about it.

The offerings of food had been a start. She'd give it a couple of days, not wanting to move too fast and scare him, then she would renew her attempts to get George to interreact with her.

Turning her mind away from her elusive neighbour, Nessa thought about what Tony from Pins to Elephants had said when she'd asked him if he knew anyone who could hang cupboard doors. Nessa had decided she might as well have a go at painting the ones she had before she went to the expense of buying new ones.

How difficult could it be?

She started by unscrewing one of them and taking it outside. The removal part was easy, but she wasn't sure whether she'd be able to get the door back on again, due to the complicated hinge. Oh, well, it was off now, so she might as well give it her best shot. After all, even if she bought new doors, she'd still have to put them on.

It was a bit breezy out in the garden, and Nessa glanced uncertainly at the bushes swaying and dancing. Might it be better to leave it until another day?

Bah, she'd get on with it. The sooner she did, the sooner she'd know where she stood, so she grabbed one of the old sheets she had used to cover everything when she painted the kitchen and placed it on the ground, flattening the long grass, before putting the cupboard door on top of it.

Then she looked at it for a while, debating how best to proceed.

She should definitely give the old wood a good scrub, because now it was in the unforgiving daylight she could see that although she'd washed all the units down on the day she'd moved in, there were faint marks on this door that hadn't come off.

Nessa put another sheet on the ground, fetched a bowl of hot soapy water and a wire soap pad and began to scrub.

After several minutes where she'd attacked both sides of the door, she was pleased with the result, so she rinsed the soap residue off and left the door to dry in the sun, while she went for a walk.

Forsaking the cliff-cove walk today, she headed to the village. She needed bread and milk and some other bits and bobs, and she intended to do a roast chicken lunch on Sunday, so she wanted to pick up the things she needed for that, too.

Thinking about eating made her think about the cafe where she'd consumed a portion of chilli and rice, and where the owner, Eleri, had given Nessa her first piece of information about her neighbours. George, she decided, was almost as much of an unknown quantity today as he had been then. She had made friends with Mairi, but she was no further forward with George.

Actually – Nessa raised a hand to shade her eyes and squinted – was that him now, walking briskly towards her?

It was, she was certain of it, and she hastened forward, smiling.

'George! Fancy meeting you!' she exclaimed.

'Fancy,' was his somewhat dry response, and he made to walk straight on by.

Nessa put out a hand, catching the arm of his jacket.

George stopped, looked at her hand, then looked up at her face.

Nessa left her hand where it was for the time being. 'What did you think of the pasties?'

'Delicious. Thank you.'

'How do you fancy coming to mine on Sunday? I'm going to cook a chicken and it'll be too much for me to eat by myself.' She hadn't intended to ask – she'd intended to give him a few days, but here he was and so was she, and speaking to him face to face was far better than yelling through his letterbox or shoving a note through it, both of which could be ignored. But, standing right in front of him, she couldn't be.

He could ignore her, but she didn't think he would. He might be reclusive and solitary, but she didn't think he was rude.

He hadn't taken his eyes off her hand where it rested lightly on the sleeve above his elbow, but when she issued her invitation his head came up and he looked her square on.

When Nessa's gaze met his, a shiver passed through her. Unable to tear herself away, she looked deep into his eyes. Something, she wasn't sure what, shimmered between them, making her tingle.

He opened his mouth. His lips were softly pink, his bottom teeth small and white; he was going to say something profound, she simply knew it...

'Then I suggest you cook less,' he said.

Nessa inhaled sharply, and quickly removed her hand from his arm.

One of George's eyes twitched. He inclined his head, almost regally. 'Good day,' he said, and began to walk away. Then he paused. Without looking around, he said, 'Or ask Mairi. She could do with having somebody cook for her.'

'What about you?' she asked swiftly, before he took another step.

She saw him stiffen and hesitate, then he carried on walking.

Nessa watched him go, hoping he'd turn around, but he didn't, and she was left wondering what had just happened. She was also left with the suspicion that he had dearly wanted to accept her offer of Sunday lunch, but hadn't known how to.

Oh well, there was more than one way to cook a spud, and she knew exactly what her next move would be.

Chapter 17

George

George should have started work by now but although he'd positioned himself at his desk and had opened the correct document, he found he was spending more time staring out of the window so as not to miss Nessa's return, than he did looking at the accounts of Messrs. Acton and Stavely Ltd.

Drat, this woman was proving to be detrimental to his business, despite being beneficial to his tastebuds.

Nessa's final pasty was still in the fridge and the thought of it was making his stomach growl, even though he had a while to go until lunchtime.

Lunch! Roast chicken, she'd said.

He shut his eyes and tried to force the image out of his mind.

Stuffing, fluffy roast potatoes, rich, smooth gravy… dear God, that woman was going to be the death of him. If her roast dinners were anything like her cakes and pasties, he would have been in for a treat.

But he'd turned her down.

He hadn't even had the courtesy to thank her for the invitation, which was unforgivable of him. But she'd taken him by surprise and there was that hand of hers on his arm where it had no business being, and it had been such an enormously long time since he'd been touched by anyone that it had thrown him.

Her eyes had thrown him too; they had stared into his with such intensity he hadn't been able to look away. They'd reminded him of the colour of the sea the other day, grey and flecked with navy and white.

He must find some way of thanking her which didn't involve a note on her doorstep. Passing notes back and forth felt childish, like pupils swapping illicit notes in class (did they still do that, he wondered, or did they just get their phones out and text one another?).

He'd have a think about it – something was bound to occur to him. Perhaps he could spare her the effort of lugging her bins to the pavement on the next rubbish collection day by putting them out for her? Or maybe not, because he might be tempted to check what she was or wasn't recycling, and he also might be tempted to rescue some of it.

Unable to concentrate, George kept shooting quick looks out of the window every few seconds. Then he tried playing a game: he promised himself he would work for five minutes before he allowed himself to take another look, but all that happened was that he spent the time he otherwise would have spent looking out of the window, watching the clock in the corner of the computer screen instead.

Throwing his hands up in the air in disgust, he went into the kitchen to make his mid-morning drink and as a result, completely missed Nessa's return. He only realised she was back when the noisy kettle switched itself off and he heard her speaking to her cat from her back garden.

'Sylvia, no,' he heard her say and he wondered what the cat was doing to make his neighbour sound cross.

The animal couldn't have got up to a great deal because its mistress had only just come home, but once again curiosity got the better of him, and George simply had to see what was going on.

And the only way to do that was to venture into his own garden and peer over the fence.

Which he had absolutely no intention of doing. Until he heard a rhythmic rattle and then the sound of someone spraying something.

He still didn't intend to go and have a look, not even when the intriguing sounds were repeated.

When he heard Nessa say loudly, 'I give up,' he was unable to resist any longer, so he cautiously opened his front door a couple of inches and peered out.

When he didn't see anyone, he opened it wide enough to squeeze through, and then slunk around the side of the bungalow, keeping low in case Nessa happened to come out of her front door and glance in his direction. She had a habit of doing that.

As soon as he reached the side gate, he unlatched it and darted through as quietly as he could in case his neighbour was still in her back garden. The rattling and spraying noises had ceased though, so she might not be, and the thought made his skin prickle. If she was in her house, she might well see him from one of her rear-facing windows, although why that should worry him he had no idea. He was perfectly entitled to be in his own garden, and if he just happened to glance into hers, what was the harm in that?

Standing straighter, he made his way up the slight slope of the path which bisected his neat lawn, and casually glanced to his right.

There was no sign of her.

Her cat sat on the fence, though, and stared at him.

He stared back.

The cat didn't flinch.

George looked away first, but he also took the opportunity to step off the path and across the lawn, holding his hand out and making the tongue-clicking noise he'd heard other pet owners make.

It didn't appear to be doing much good when it came to the cat, but at least it made him seem like he was trying to make friends with the animal and not sneak a look into Nessa's garden, which was what he was actually trying to do.

Nessa wasn't in it.

What *was* in it was a sheet flattening the overly-long grass, and what looked like a half-painted cupboard door sitting in the centre of the fabric. Next to it was a can of spray paint lying on its side with the cap off.

George studied the cupboard door, his head cocked slightly to the side.

Although he was aware of the cat sniffing his outstretched hand and the tickle of its long whiskers, his concentration was taken by the badly applied paint. To him, it looked like she'd sprayed it on too thickly in places so it had congealed in some parts and run in others, and the rest of her attempt had not been thick enough. Patchy was an understatement.

He looked again.

Nessa hadn't taken the metal knob off, and splattered paint had turned it into an unsightly mess. It was also rather rusty, which didn't help the situation.

She'd made a pig's ear of the job, that was for sure.

The cat seemed to think so too, because now it had finished sniffing his hand, it turned its attention to the eyesore in its garden.

'Not good, is it?' George said to the cat.

The cat blinked one eye, then turned its back on him and jumped down into its own garden. It stalked over to the cupboard door, sniffed, then stuck its tail in the air and sauntered off, giving George a view of its behind.

'My thoughts exactly,' he said to it.

Then he realised two things simultaneously; one, he was talking to a cat – something he'd never done in his life before; and two, he was in full view of Nessa, should she decide to look out of her window.

With a strangled squawk, he briskly stepped back, nearly losing his balance on the grass, turned around and hurried back inside.

But as he went, a plan began to form and take shape in his mind.

Chapter 18

George

George had always looked on nightfall as a friend. As a child it was a time when he was safely tucked up in his own home, usually with a book for company. As he grew older and moved away, the night wasn't quite the sanctuary it had once been – busy cities never slept – but he embraced it, nevertheless.

Tonight, he positively revelled in it, because without its soft cloak, he'd be clearly visible from Nessa's house and probably from Mairi's, too. He wasn't so bothered about anyone else along the row of semi-detached cottages seeing him – they didn't show any interest in him, nor he them. Which was just the way he liked it.

It wasn't easy clambering over the fence separating Nessa's garden from his, but it was a darned sight better than trying to force his way through a hedge. He recalled his father's objections when Alys had employed three burly men to remove the hedge and replace it with a sturdy featherboard fence. There was nothing his father could do, as the boundary was Alys's responsibility, and she could no longer manage to maintain the hedge herself. Unless his father intended to trim it every couple of weeks throughout the growing season, then the Nightingales had had to put up with the new fence.

The construction had taken place before George had moved home, but even back then his father wasn't in any fit state to cut a hedge. Alys used to get a man in to do the front, but since she'd died, George had cut it. It was due a trim now.

Perhaps he'd tackle it tomorrow if he saw Nessa go out. Just his side and the top; he didn't want anyone saying his standards had slipped, although he'd do her side for her as well if he had enough time. And by that, he meant if Nessa was out for long enough. He'd probably get it done if she took the clifftop walk which he'd seen her do.

He managed to haul himself up and over the fence, his boot-clad toes scrabbling for purchase on the rough wood, and he dropped down into her garden with a grunt.

Now all he had to do was grab the cupboard door and return to his own property without getting caught. Which was easier said than done when you were nearly sixty, unused to clambering about over fences, and holding a ruddy great lump of wood.

In the end he flung the cupboard door over the fence to land on his lawn, so he only had himself to worry about. It wasn't as though he was going to damage its paintwork, was it? Damage might be an improvement on Nessa's handiwork.

He didn't change his mind after he'd scrambled back into his own garden and was able to examine the door properly. It would need sanding down completely, a coat of primer, and at least one, if not two, layers of topcoat.

He'd not be able to do any of that in the bungalow and neither was he able to use the shed or the garage, and although the breeze earlier in the day had abated, it was still there. Paint didn't like flying leaves or dust, therefore he needed to find a sheltered spot outside.

George switched on the outside light, stood on the paved area outside the kitchen window and looked around, tapping a finger against his chin as he considered his options, before finally deciding the most sheltered place was the area between the shed and the garage, where Nessa's fence provided a third barrier.

And boy, was George grateful for that fence now. Not only did it screen the area from the winds which blew in from the sea, but it also hid his collection of plastic milk bottles from his neighbour.

It was the best place to work on Nessa's cupboard door. But first, he had to do something with those darned cartons, and it was a dilemma he could do without. He had nowhere else to put them.

He did have a silly moment when he thought about his totally empty and pristine plastic recycling bin, but he shoved the thought away as soon as it popped into his head. However, he needed to put them somewhere, otherwise he may as well throw Nessa's cupboard door back over the fence and walk away.

Nessa… recycling…? Ah ha! Her boxes, her lovely big cardboard boxes which had been destined for the bin lorry until he'd spotted them and given them a reprieve. Now *they* could be useful – they could have a temporary new lease of life as plastic milk carton receptacles. Genius!

He'd have to empty them out again of course, when he was done painting her door, because they'd soon disintegrate when faced with the next fall of Welsh rain, but for now it was a perfect solution, so he quickly reconstructed them. Then he proceeded to put as many cartons in each one as he could. Once that was done, he stacked the boxes neatly beneath the kitchen window and began his real task for the evening.

As he worked (sanding was far more satisfying than he remembered it being), his mind wandered to thoughts of the woman next door. He still had a lingering suspicion she was sticking her nose in his business, but he stamped down on it. Nosey or not, it was kind of her to invite him for lunch, and it had been kind of her to give him cake and pasties.

There, that was better. George stood back to have a look at his work, the door now had a perfect base for a coat of primer. The primer was quick-drying, so he would be able to put the topcoat on early tomorrow morning. If he could find it. There were so many pots of paint in the shed, nearly all of them half-empty, but he thought most of them were right at the back, where there was little hope of ever reaching them.

He had to look though, but he would need a light. He owned a decent torch, but it was in the cupboard nearest the back door and he hadn't been able to get to that for at least two years, maybe longer, so he grabbed one of the many boxes of matches from the only drawer in the dresser he could get to and hurried outside to find the paint.

It took a while, but eventually, after a great deal of shifting and moving things about, he found what he was looking for – a nearly full tin of everyday white primer and a third of a tin of furniture paint. God knows how old the tin of furniture paint was, because he couldn't remember his father ever using it for anything, but when George prised the lid off, he saw it was still good – nothing a thorough stir couldn't remedy.

And as he pained the primer on and made plans for an early start in the morning, George felt his father's mantra of waste not, want not had served him very well indeed today.

All he hoped was that Nessa would like mint-green cupboard doors.

Chapter 19

Nessa

Nessa was cross with herself. She was cross she hadn't been able to complete a relatively simple task like splodging some paint on some wood. She was also annoyed that she had bothered to try in the first place, because she now had an even uglier cupboard door than she'd had to start with, *and* she had to face the task of trying to rehang the blessed thing.

She also hoped it hadn't rained in the night and soaked the wood. She might not be very DIY-minded, but she knew enough to realise wet wood could swell and distort and she could have kicked herself for not fetching it inside.

Nessa intended to have breakfast before she went outside to check on the state of the poor door, but as she entered her kitchen her eyes automatically went to the gaping hole in the run of cupboard doors, the contents of that cupboard on display for anyone who cared to look. She knew she was being ridiculous because it was only her (and possibly Mairi) who would see it, but it went against her nature. She hated mess. And being able to see the plates, bowls and other china which was stored in there was rather irksome, despite the crockery being neatly stacked.

She went to the sink and filled the kettle, yawning as she did so, then froze, mid-yawn, letting the air in her lungs out slowly as she scanned the lawn.

The cupboard door wasn't there.

As she waited for the kettle to boil, she went outside to check around the garden in case she'd moved it from the lawn. She also took a look at her garden gate.

It was still locked, and there was no sign of anyone having climbed over it, so she discounted the idea of burglars. Anyway, no one would make the effort of getting into her garden and then only taking a ruined cupboard door.

Nessa tilted her head to the side as she thought hard.

Had she brought it inside and had forgotten she'd done so?

Feeling rather silly, because she *knew* she'd left it on the lawn, Nessa nonetheless did a quick tour of the house. When she still couldn't find the door, she returned to the kitchen, drank a cup of tea and tried to figure out what could have possibly happened to it.

There must be another explanation, but she couldn't think of one, and it continued to play on her mind while she got ready for her morning walk.

Debating whether to take a shower-proof jacket with her, Nessa opened her front door to take a good look at the sky. The front of the cottage faced west, where the prevailing winds came from, and it was becoming her habit to check whether there was any weather sweeping in off the Irish Sea before she went out. But something else caught her attention instead.

There, propped up against the side of her house was a cupboard door!

It was the same size and shape as the one she'd been trying to paint yesterday, but that was where the similarity ended.

Her door had been half dark pine and half splodgy white.

This one was mint green and there wasn't a splodge, a drip or a run in sight, as far as she could tell without examining it closely.

Nessa looked up and down the lane, as if she expected whoever had left it there to still be around, but there was no one.

Anyway, she had a jolly good idea who had done this and she guessed if she looked at the bungalow next door, George may well be staring back at her. Not that she'd be able to see him through those thick net curtains, but she'd know.

With her index finger Nessa checked that the paint was dry before she picked up the door and took it inside for a closer look.

Green, I ask you! she thought.

What had got into him? He could see she wanted it white, and although she appreciated the intention behind his actions, what she didn't appreciate was the colour. Whoever heard of green units!

It was a light cheery green, admittedly, but green was green.

Nessa had wanted white.

With a deep sigh and wondering how she was going to remove the paint (or whether she'd bite the bullet and order some new ones online), she put it down in front of the cupboard it belonged to.

Then she shook her head, closed her eyes and took a deep breath; she wasn't looking forward to this, but she had to tackle George about it. Not only had he somehow got into her garden, he'd also not asked her permission to paint the door. If he'd had asked, she would have taken him up on the offer with alacrity, with the proviso that the colour he used was white.

Nessa opened her eyes again, and they were immediately drawn to the green cupboard door.

Hang on a sec…

It looked rather nice, picking out the green in the curtains and the cushions. It complemented the nearly white-with-a-hint-of-lavender walls, and even with only the one door painted, her kitchen looked lighter already.

But she'd wanted white, not green. And he hadn't asked.

Nessa checked the time.

In approximately seven minutes George should be walking down the pavement past her house. She'd tackle him then, rather than try to get him to answer his door. So she perched her backside on the arm of the chair which sat underneath the window in her living room and waited.

Ten minutes later she was still waiting.

She checked the time again, comparing the watch on her wrist to the clock on the mantelpiece. They both said the same.

She waited another ten minutes before coming to the conclusion he'd either gone out earlier, or he wasn't going out at all. She guessed it was the latter, and she also guessed the reason why – he didn't want to risk bumping into her.

Should she knock on his door? Would it do any good?

Probably not, but she had to vent her feelings to someone, so she stalked to Mairi's house, all the while shooting evil looks in the general direction of the bungalow.

'Hello, dear, I was about to have a cup of tea. Would you like to join me?' Mairi asked as soon as she saw Nessa.

'I'd love to, although I could do with something stronger right now.'

'Why, what's wrong?' Mairi led her into the kitchen and gestured for Nessa to sit down.

'George,' Nessa said, taking a seat.

'What's happened?'

'He painted one of my kitchen cupboard doors.'

'That was nice of him.' Mairi looked surprised.

'Yes, I suppose it was, but he did it without asking.'

'Oh. I take it, you didn't want it painted?' The surprise had morphed into concern. 'Oh, dear.'

'Well, yes, I did… I'd had a go at doing it myself yesterday, but I made a right hash of it.'

'I don't understand – did George make an even bigger mess of it?' She poured the tea and gave Nessa a cup.

'Thanks,' she said, then added, 'Not at all. He did a sterling job.'

'So what's the problem?'

Conscious of Mairi's confused expression, Nessa said, 'I was painting it white. George painted it green.'

'Ooh, that sounds charming. I bet it looks nice; I always did like green. It's such a restful colour.'

'Yeah, that's why so many hospital walls are painted green,' Nessa said.

'Oh, it's not NHS green, is it? No wonder you're not happy. It's not the nicest colour in the world.'

'Actually, it's mint green. There's not even a whiff of the NHS about it.'

'Can I take a look?'

'If you like.'

Nessa and Mairi finished their drinks, then Nessa took her neighbour to her house and stood back to let her examine the cupboard door.

'I must say, I think it's rather nice.' Mairi's opinion came after a short pause. 'It's lovely and fresh. Imagine the whole lot in this colour.'

Nessa imagined. 'Will it go with the worktops, do you think?'

'Hold it up and let's see.'

Nessa held the door directly next to the pine worktop. 'Hmm, I'm not sure.'

'The worktop is wood, isn't it?' Mairi asked.

'I think so.' Nessa bent down for a closer look. 'Yes, I believe it is.'

'Then it can be sanded down and re-stained if needs be, although I think it looks fine as it is.'

'Do you?'

Mairi nodded. 'I do, and not only that, but it's also better than scrapping the whole lot and starting again. I remember when Alys had this kitchen put in. It must have been over thirty years ago, and all the cupboards were handmade – none of this flat-packed stuff.' Mairi ran a hand across the surface of the worktop nearest her. 'Good quality, this is. All it needs is a lick of paint.' She gave Nessa a pointed look.

Nessa sighed. 'Just like George has done?'

'Bingo!'

'But—'

'But what? You said yourself the colour is quite nice. Is it because he didn't ask your permission?'

'Maybe.' Nessa shrugged.

'He should have asked,' Mairi agreed, 'but try to take it in the spirit it was meant. In fact, you're honoured; I can't recall the last time he did much more than exchange good morning with anyone.'

Nessa was now beginning to wonder if she'd overreacted. It *was* nice of him, she conceded, and the colour was definitely growing on her. It was almost as though she'd brought some of the garden inside, especially with the lavender flowers and green leaf of the soft furnishings.

'That means I must be making some progress with him.' Nessa, in her irritation, had failed to see it that way, and she was grateful to Mairi for pointing it out.

'Give him time. And some space. Don't forget, he's been reclusive for so long, it's going to take more than giving him a cake to bring him round.'

Nessa had done a bit more than simply giving him a cake, and she felt guilty she hadn't taken Mairi some of the baked goods as well when she'd made the pasties the other day. She thought of asking her to Sunday lunch, but she was hoping when George smelt the chicken roasting she might be able to tempt him out, and having Mairi there might scare him off. She could always take Mairi a plate later.

'I'm going to need some new knobs,' Nessa said, scrutinising the one she'd managed to get paint all over and which George (bless him) had cleaned off. They were horrid round metal ones which had seen better days. She quite fancied some antique-style glass or ceramic ones that she'd spotted in a magazine once, gracing the front of a Welsh dresser.

'Yes, I think you're right. You could try Pins to Elephants, or there's a boot sale just outside Applewell tomorrow. They have craft stalls there, too. You never know what you might pick up. It's ages since I've been — it's a bit too far for my old legs.'

'Why don't I take you? Unless you've got other plans for the weekend?'

'No, no plans. My daughter is in Italy on holiday, so I expect it'll be a couple of weeks before I see her again.'

'I've got no plans either, so we can keep each other company. What time do you want me to pick you up?' If Nessa was going on her own she'd walk to the car boot sale site, but she'd happily drive to it if it meant Mairi could accompany her.

'Nine? We can get there before it's too busy.' Mairi made to leave, but Nessa wanted her for something else, too.

'Do you have a lawnmower I can borrow? My house in Bristol didn't have a garden and if I don't tackle the wilderness soon, I dread to think what might be living in there.'

'Of course, my dear, but I must warn you, it's not one of those new-fangled electric hover things. It's a push-along and it hasn't been used for years, so the blades are probably all rusty.'

'I'm sure I'll manage, and I'll run the mower over yours too, if you like.'

'Would you, dear? That's so kind of you.'

Nessa gave her a quick kiss on the cheek. 'My pleasure,' she said.

And it was. Helping others was in her blood, and if there was one person who could do with her help, it was Mairi.

Another person she knew of was George, but helping *him* wasn't going to be as straightforward as mowing his lawn or accompanying him to a boot sale.

Chapter 20

George

George fully expected Nessa to hightail it to his house as soon as she saw the cupboard door which he'd left propped up on her step, and he steeled himself for first a knock, followed by a shout through the letterbox when he failed to answer. Therefore, he was rather disappointed when, after she'd taken it inside, she reappeared and went to Mairi's house. Did she think the old lady was responsible for the paint job?

She came back out, accompanied by Mairi, and both of them went into Nessa's house, then after a short while, Mairi reappeared and went back home.

It was like a revolving door out there with all the comings and goings, and George was fascinated. Apart from a couple of dog walkers and the occasional farm vehicle, there had never been much to see in the lane in terms of human activity until Nessa had moved in. Now it was a regular hive of busyness.

It was taking him twice as long as it normally would to get a set of accounts done, and after Mairi left Nessa's house he gave himself a stern talking-to. It didn't help that he was unable to settle properly because he had deviated from his routine *again* last night, spending half of it working on a cupboard door that wasn't even his. This

140

morning he'd got up ridiculously early to finish the job and had forgone his morning walk as a result.

The lack of it, and not having purchased a newspaper, weighed heavily on his mind, but not as heavily as Nessa ignoring his efforts.

No wonder he preferred his own company to that of other people.

Disappointment stabbed him in the chest, and he switched his computer on and began to do what he was paid to do. But before he could get into his stride, he noticed movement in the lane and he glanced out of the window to see Nessa walking along the pavement and then turning into his drive.

Flustered, he leapt to his feet, became unbalanced, and smacked into the wall beside him.

Thanking his lucky stars he hadn't fallen the other way and knocked a stack of books over (the resultant carnage didn't bear thinking about – it had taken him ages to clear up the last time), he hurried into the hall as best he could, whilst making sure not to brush up against anything similarly precarious. He arrived at his front door at the same moment Nessa banged out a rat-tat-tattoo on it.

George jumped and let out a muted squeak, then clapped a hand to his mouth, scared she had heard him.

The letterbox rattled as she lifted it. 'George? Are you in there?'

He shook his head. She didn't sound friendly.

'I just wanted to thank you for painting my cupboard door. It was a very kind thing to do.'

George blew out a sigh and some of the tension drained out of him. She wasn't cross; that was a relief.

'I'm about to mow mine and Mairi's lawn,' she shouted. 'Would you like me to do yours at the same time?'

No, he wouldn't. He was perfectly capable of doing his own lawn, although he hadn't touched either the front or the back since Nessa had moved in (in case she saw him and thought it was a good idea to pop out for a chat), and it was now in dire need of a trim. As was his hair, now he came to think of it. He ran his fingers through the offending locks, which were still relatively thick despite receding a little at the temples, and wondered why she was still talking to him when he clearly wasn't at home.

Except, he was, wasn't he, and he had a suspicion she knew it.

Nevertheless, he stayed silent and hoped she'd go away soon.

'The invitation to lunch on Sunday still stands,' she called. 'Roast chicken with all the trimmings? Just you and me?' A pause, then, 'I... erm... meant there would be no one else, although I could invite Mairi if it makes you feel better. About not being alone with me, I mean.' Then he heard her mutter, 'Bugger.'

He heard her footsteps recede down the path and he chuckled.

Suddenly he paused, startled at the unfamiliar noise coming from his throat. He'd been known to utter a polite laugh or two when the occasion warranted it, but he couldn't bring to mind the last time he'd done so voluntarily, and a chuckle at that.

But she was amusing, even if she hadn't meant to be.

He wondered if she'd blushed as she said it. He also wondered what eating lunch together, just him and her, would be like.

He almost wished he could find out.

It took him a while to return to his chair in the corner of the living room, and it took him even longer to turn his mind away from imagined images of his neighbour with pink on her cheeks and embarrassment in her eyes. But when he eventually did, it wasn't long before he was once again dragged out of the world of databases and spreadsheets and into what was happening in Nessa Millbrook's back garden.

He had heard a sound similar to a chainsaw with breathing difficulties, followed by a yelp and cursing.

He listened intently, and the noises came again.

Unable to stop himself, he got up from his chair and padded to the kitchen window, where he could just about see Nessa pushing an ancient lawnmower. She was doing so with great difficulty and her cheeks were as pink as he thought they might have been when she had been standing on the other side of his front door earlier.

He watched as she tried to push the mower through grass which was far too long to be cut without using a strimmer first, and he itched to take it from her and do it himself. He also itched to get his hands on the old machine whose blades, he suspected, were blunt. It could do with being sent to a company which specialised in just such a thing, but it was doubtful if they'd even look at such an old one.

He did, however, have a whetstone in the garage. He remembered his father using it when he was a child to put sharp edges back on shovels and shears. All that was needed was a bit of water and some elbow grease. He wouldn't even have to dismantle the blades, although it would be easier to work on them—

143

George was pulled out of his daydream by another curse from the lady next door, and he suppressed a grin. Who knew she could swear like that? She looked so genteel and middle-class, yet she was calling the recalcitrant mower all the names under the sun. Not really bad names, not like some of the names he'd been called in his youth, but still the curses weren't what he'd expected to hear coming from his neighbour's lips.

She had nice lips, full and soft, and they smiled readily and often. What would it be like to kiss them, he mused?

Abruptly, he spun away from the window, alarm washing over him.

Dear God, what was he thinking?

This wasn't like him at all. He didn't have thoughts like that any more. Not since his much younger days when he had enough emotional strength to date.

In university he'd met like-minded people, young men and women who'd understood his nerdiness. A few of the men had turned into friends, and several of the women had turned into lovers, but the relationships hadn't lasted, and gradually he'd come to believe he was better off without the hassle of dating.

Life was easier and less hurtful that way.

And now that he'd been incarcerated in his parents' house for the previous ten or more years, he wasn't the remotest bit interested in any relationship of any kind. He was past all that nonsense. Besides, who would look twice at an odd codger like him?

Nessa Millbrook wouldn't, that was for sure.

No wonder she'd got all embarrassed when she'd thought she'd invited him on a date.

But as he watched her continue to try to haul the blunt mower through grass far too long for it to cope with, he felt a brief pang — even if Nessa did look at him twice, there was no way he'd be able to allow himself to do anything about it.

Chapter 21

Nessa

'Is that Nessa Millbrook?' a female voice asked when Nessa answered her phone an hour or so later. She was hot, sweaty, tired, and incredibly cross. That damned lawnmower was going to be the death of her. She'd be better off going to Pins to Elephants and seeing if they had any in stock and buy herself a new one – after all, they seemed to have everything else.

'Yes, this is she.'

'It's Gracie Stewart – I shortened your curtains for you?'

'Oh yes, I remember. How are you?'

'Good thanks. You're probably wondering why I'm calling, and I wouldn't normally bother you, but I'm at the newsagents and Sid – he's the owner – was talking about your neighbour, George, and saying he hadn't been in for his newspaper today, and he was wondering if he was OK.' Gracie ground to a halt.

'Oh, right.'

'As I had your number from when we arranged for the curtains to be altered, I volunteered to give you a call because Sid hoped you'd be able to pop to George's house and check on him. Sid says he's not missed buying a paper in years and he's worried about him.'

'I see. I think he's OK,' Nessa replied, although she was feeling a little doubtful. 'But I'll go round and check, then call you back. Give me a few minutes.'

And with that, Nessa washed her hands, splashed some water on her face, and darted out of the door, praying nothing had happened to her reclusive and somewhat annoying neighbour.

'George! Are you in there? George! Answer the door! George! *George!*' she yelled, probably louder than she should have done.

And suddenly he was there, yanking his door open, a worried look on his face. 'What's wrong?' he demanded. He took a step towards her and she had the impression he was ready to dash to her aid if necessary.

Nessa gave him a huge smile. 'You're OK!' she exclaimed with relief. Despite knowing he was more than likely fine, she was nevertheless thankful to see for herself. Gracie's call had made her worry unnecessarily.

'Why wouldn't I be?'

'Gracie Stewart and Sid from the newsagent were worried something awful had happened to you.'

George screwed up his eyes and squinted at her. 'As you can see, I am perfectly well.' He shook his head and she thought he might be exasperated with her.

She had to admit, it had been rather over the top for Gracie to call her. Surely someone could miss buying a newspaper for one day without causing such a fuss?

'Why were Gracie and Sid—?' he began, then abruptly stopped talking as she let out a gasp.

In his haste to answer her frantic knocking, he'd opened his front door wider than he'd probably meant to, and it had taken her a moment for what she saw to sink in. She'd been so relieved to find George alive and well, she hadn't initially noticed the state of the hallway behind, then her brain caught up with her eyes — paper, stacks and stacks of paper, with a narrow walkway just wide enough for a person to negotiate — and her attention flickered back to George and the horrified expression on his face.

Dear God, so that's what the poor man—

He took a lurching step back inside, and Nessa flinched and tottered backwards as the door was slammed in her face, almost squashing her nose.

She stood there, uncertainly, not sure how she should react, or what she should say. But she surely had to do *something*. She could hardly walk away and pretend she'd not seen the state of George's hall.

Nessa heaved in a deep breath and knocked again. This time the sound was more tentative, unlike her frantic thumping of a few minutes ago. 'George? Open the door.'

Nothing.

She even put her ear to the heavily-frosted glass but she didn't hear a thing.

Crouching down, she lifted the flap on the letterbox. 'George,' she called, louder this time, feeling idiotic. 'Let's talk about this.'

Still nothing.

'Don't be embarrassed. I can help you, if you want?' she shouted. If the rest of his house was anything like the hall, George was going to need all the help he could get, and then some. It had looked like some kind of cave in there with only a speck of light at the far end. No wonder he was so secretive.

Nessa yearned to get her hands on those ceiling-high towers of what had appeared to be newspapers, and an image of her hands encased in Marigolds and wielding a black plastic bag swam into her head. It would take some doing and many trips to the local recycling centre, but sorting it out could be done. And the sooner it was tackled, the better off George would be, in her opinion. He couldn't possibly be happy living like that.

'George!' Aware her tone was edging from persuasive to irritated, she repeated his name, softer this time. 'George, I can help. Please let me help.'

She listened again.

He wasn't going to answer, was he?

Finally, Nessa had no alternative other than to walk away.

'Gracie? It's Nessa,' she said, holding the phone to her ear as she walked into her own neat little hall and compared it to the mess she'd just seen. 'I've just spoken to George. He's fine. I expect he'll be fetching his paper as usual tomorrow.'

'That's a weight off my mind – and Sid's. Did he say why he didn't come into the village this morning?'

'No, and I didn't ask.' She hadn't had the chance to – he'd slammed the door shut with such speed it had taken her breath away.

Dear God, she still couldn't believe what she'd seen. How he managed to negotiate his hallway was beyond her comprehension. She wanted to think that it was just the one space which was crammed to the rafters, but she had an awful suspicion the rest of the house would be as bad.

No wonder he never opened the door to her.

She felt awful that her visit today had alarmed him to such an extent that he'd let his guard down. They had both been as shocked as each other, she thought. Her heart was still pounding and she felt unsteady. His reaction had upset her, but she realised he probably needed time to process what had just happened. She was desperate to go over to his house and try to explain that she was here for him, but she thought it might be best if she left him to it for a while. He'd come round eventually, especially when he realised she only wanted to help.

Despite vowing to hang back, she wanted nothing more than to scoop him into her arms and soothe his tortured soul.

But when the image of her doing her Florence Nightingale bit and stroking George's furrowed brow transformed itself into her kissing that brow, then his lips coming up to meet hers, Nessa had to give herself a very stern talking-to indeed.

Chapter 22

George

George hadn't had the best night's sleep. He didn't think he'd slept at all, having clock-watched from what seemed like the minute he'd fallen into bed to the minute he'd decided enough was enough and he may as well get up.

He blamed his lack of shut-eye solely on Nessa Millbrook. Fear swept over him, drenching him in cold dread. Dear God, she'd seen the state of his house. She'd seen inside! No one had done that in years. *No one.*

If she hadn't come banging on his door yesterday, he wouldn't have thought there was something wrong, and he wouldn't have forgotten himself and...

Who was he kidding? Things had started to go pear-shaped long before yesterday. It had started the day she moved in. He hadn't known a minute's peace since Mrs Hayworth had gleefully informed him he had a new neighbour.

It had been downhill since then.

But what had kept him awake for most (all) of last night, was the dread Nessa would tell someone (many someones?) what she had seen when she'd looked past him into his hall, horror, disgust and pity vying for supremacy on her face.

Her expression would haunt him for the rest of his days.

See, this was the reason he didn't allow anyone to get close to him. People judged. People were cruel, and the second you opened yourself up and let one of them in, you were liable to be hurt.

And now his private business would be broadcast all over the village to whoever cared to hear it – and he well knew that in a small place like Applewell, everyone wanted to know everyone else's business.

Who would she tell first? That Gracie-woman who had asked her to check up on him? Sid? Or, and this was more likely, she'd start with Mairi, as they were fast becoming bosom friends.

Hell, how would he be able to hold his head up in the village again?

George leant against the wall by the microwave and put his head in his hands.

Dear God, how had his life come to this?

What had he done to deserve it?

Those boys were right. Everyone was right. They'd said he was a loser, and he was. They'd called him weird, and he was.

They didn't call him anything now, but that was only because George never went to Lampeter. He hadn't stepped foot in the town since his last official day in school, never mind that the kids had come from all over. Only one boy in Applewell had joined in with the name-calling and the pushing, but he was a man now, with a wife, kids of his own and grandchildren, and George rarely bumped into him. Which was just the way he liked it. Tell a lie, he had come into contact with him shortly after he'd moved back into the bungalow to look after his father. The man's name was Gareth Lewis, and he'd given George a nod, and had said, 'Sorry to hear about your mam.' And that

152

had been it. Gareth had hardly acknowledged him, had hardly remembered him. Which was worse somehow, as though the way he'd treated George, the misery which that boy had subjected him to had had no bearing on the man he'd become. It was as though Gareth Lewis had forgotten what he had done.

But George hadn't forgotten.

He might have moved on, but he hadn't forgotten.

He never would. He wasn't entirely sure he'd forgiven Gareth, although he had tried.

And if Nessa spread his business all over Applewell, then she was no better than Gareth Lewis and the rest of those bullies, and he'd never forgive her either.

It was time he had breakfast, but when he reached for the box of cereal, he didn't have any appetite, although he did manage a cup of tea. His tummy gurgled and protested as he drank, the hot liquid doing nothing to quell the queasiness he felt at the thought of going into the village for his newspaper.

Could he do without it?

He could; he'd done without one yesterday, therefore he didn't need to buy one today.

But his stomach clenched anew at the thought of not buying a newspaper. He'd be out of routine yet again. Yesterday's disruption had been difficult enough to cope with. Today, more than any other, he needed the familiarity of his daily schedule.

But before he slotted back into it (he didn't want to think about how he'd react if his morning visit to Sid's was filled with pitying looks and whispered comments from hand-covered mouths), there was one thing he had to do.

Decision made, George dressed with his usual care; he didn't want to give anyone any more reason to feel

153

sorry for him. Then he squeezed out of his front door, making double-sure no one could see inside even though Oak Lane was deserted, and walked purposefully down his drive, along the pavement and onto Nessa's property.

His heart was banging harder than Nessa had pounded on his door yesterday and his mouth was dry, but this had to be done. He had to say what was in his mind before he could move on. He'd fretted and worried enough, he'd let her disrupt his life for too long. It was time he told her so.

She must have seen him coming. She must have been watching for him, because she'd opened her door before he reached it and was standing on her step with a smile on her face, her own front door open wide, allowing him to see inside, the receding hallway mocking him with its clean lines and emptiness.

'George,' she gushed. 'I was just coming to see you.'

'I bet you were,' he said. 'Wanting to get another look to make sure of your facts before you go ahead and spread my business all over the village, I expect.'

Her smile faded and she shook her head. 'I... um...'

'Ah, I see – you've already told everyone.'

'No! I—'

'Let me tell you something, Nessa Millbrook. You've been the bane of my life since you moved into this house. Nothing but a nuisance with your nosiness and your interfering ways. I don't appreciate it. But what I would appreciate is, if you'd mind your own business and stay out of mine.'

'I haven't said anything to anyone about... you know.' She jerked her head towards his bungalow.

Damn her, she couldn't even bring herself to say what she meant, that's how disgusted she was. He shook his head and turned to leave.

'Sorry,' she whispered. 'I didn't realise I was being a nuisance. I was just trying to be friendly.' She sounded so contrite, so upset, he almost told her it was OK.

But it wasn't OK. *He* wasn't OK, and it was all because of her.

With his back to her, he said, 'I don't want your friendship. Not yours, not anyone's. I'm fine just the way I am, so stop sticking your nose in where it's not wanted.'

There, that told her, he thought, as he marched into the village, his head held high as he refused to meet anyone's gaze. A nod was all he was prepared to give this morning. He'd given her a piece of his mind, told her what he'd thought. He grunted; he was quite sure she'd not bother him again.

But if that was the case, why didn't it make him feel better?

Chapter 23

Nessa

Nessa stumbled back inside her neat comfortable cottage, her mind whirling, her emotions all over the place. All she'd been trying to do was to make friends and be neighbourly, and he'd thrown it back in her face. She was used to patients not being grateful (often because they were confused, or frightened, or had been brought to hospital against their will), but that had been at work. This was different. This was personal.

Upset didn't begin to describe how she was feeling right now.

How dare he? And for his information she had no intention of telling anyone anything about the inside of his bungalow. He clearly had issues, but they were his issues to share, not hers. She knew all about discretion and confidentiality, thank you very much; she didn't need him reminding her.

As she got ready to take Mairi to the car boot sale, she banged her things down and slammed about, until she gradually calmed down. Maybe she was overreacting (she was, she knew she was), but she hadn't been prepared for a confrontation, and he'd taken her completely by surprise. She understood he was scared she'd tell every Tom, Dick and Harry about his living conditions, but he could have just asked her not to, instead of flying off the handle.

His fear was one thing, and she could forgive him for that. But what she couldn't forgive were the things he'd said. She didn't think she was in the least bit nosey, and if being kind enough to give someone some baked goods and inviting them for a meal was considered to be interfering then she was guilty as charged.

'Do you think I'm interfering?' she asked Mairi once the pair of them were safely inside Nessa's car and there was no chance of George overhearing their conversation. She bristled as she remembered the occasions she'd been convinced he was peering out at her from behind his thick net curtains. No wonder they were thick – they needed to be to hide the clutter that was probably in every room. Talk about the pot calling the kettle black! He took the biscuit when it came to nosiness. Look at what he'd done with her cupboard door. If that wasn't being nosey and interfering, she didn't know what was.

'What makes you say that?' Mairi asked, struggling to clip in her seatbelt.

Nessa reached over and did it for her. 'Just something someone said,' was her cautious reply. She dearly wanted to confide in her new friend but, despite what George thought of her, she didn't intend to share any details about the inside of his bungalow, and if she told Mairi it was George who had said such a hurtful thing then she'd have to explain why he'd said it.

'I don't think you're interfering at all,' Mairi said, smiling at her gratefully, 'but without knowing the circumstances that led to it being said, I can't really comment.'

'Fair enough. I can't tell you, although I'd like to.'

Mairi patted her on the knee. 'You've been nothing but kind to me, my dear, but not all people see kindness for what it is.'

Nessa gave her a sharp look. Had Mairi overheard her and George's altercation earlier? She wanted to ask but didn't dare, because that would give the game away.

'Are you looking for anything in particular today?' she asked instead, changing the subject.

Mairi stared at her for a moment. 'Not really. At my age there's not a lot I need. I just like seeing the things other people want to get rid of. One of these days I'll sort my attic out – I bet I could fill a couple of car boots without making a dent.'

'If you want a hand...' Nessa offered. 'I'm good at clearing attics. I couldn't believe the amount of stuff I'd accumulated in my old one in Bristol, and I'm usually quite cutthroat when it comes to throwing things out. Apart from Christmas decorations and seasonal clothes like gloves or sun tops, then my mantra is that if I haven't used it in six months then I'm probably never going to use it, so I might as well get rid.'

This earned her another long look from her friend, before Mairi said, 'Some things are hard to let go of.'

'I know – I'm not completely ruthless; I still have a pressed flower from my mum's wedding bouquet and other sentimental items.'

'Is your mum still around?'

Nessa smiled sadly. 'No, she and dad went a few years ago within a couple of months of each other. Him first, then her. I think she died of a broken heart, although the doctors said it was an aneurysm. Their passing was one of the reasons I decided to take early retirement. Being a nurse is hard work, especially in an emergency room. I felt I needed to live a bit, before I was too old to enjoy life.'

'Thanks,' Mairi's voice was dry.

'Oh, I didn't mean… you're not…'

'Don't worry, I know what you meant, and you're right. Although I do get the impression you loved your job.'

'I did, and I was sad to leave, but I felt I'd given all I could. It was time to slow down a bit.'

'And how is that working out for you?'

The question seemed innocent enough on the surface, but Nessa could have sworn there was an undercurrent to it.

'Good, good,' she answered vaguely, keeping her eyes firmly on the road ahead. 'You'll let me know when we need to turn off, won't you?' Nessa knew she was changing the subject yet again, and she knew Mairi was also aware of it, but she didn't want to go down that rabbit hole right now.

'Take a left at the next junction, then the first right and you can't miss it. The boot sale is in the first field and there's parking in the field next to that.'

'Thank goodness it's not muddy,' Nessa said when they bumped along the uneven ground a couple of minutes later. 'I'd hate to get stuck.' The field was a large one with long clumps of grass and rutted tracks from previous vehicles.

She pulled up next to a white van and got out to give Mairi a hand.

'The farmer who owns these fields has got a tractor he uses to pull people out when they get stuck,' Mairi said. 'And talking of farmers, there's John Porter and his wife, Angharad. Cooeee!!'

Nessa smiled as they approached the couple, hissing out of the corner of her mouth, 'Is he the man who owns the farm at the end of our lane?'

Mairi nodded. 'I was just telling Nessa here that you own Porter's Farm at the end of our lane. Got a few cows and some sheep. John, Angharad, this is my new neighbour, Nessa Millbrook.'

The three of them shook hands, while Mairi beamed at them. 'Have you brought anything to sell?' the old lady asked, then added for Nessa's benefit, 'They do organic milk, butter and cheese, and free-range eggs. And don't get me started on their yoghurts.'

'You must pop up to the farm and try some,' Angharad offered and Nessa promised she would.

'No, we're not selling today,' John said. 'We're after milk churns, the old-style ones for the farm shop.'

'Farm shop?' Mairi's eyes lit up.

'We're converting one of the old sheds into a shop. The planning permission has just been approved and Angharad is in full-on renovation mode. She wants it to look oldy-worldly – whatever that is.'

Angharad elbowed him. 'You know exactly what it means – it was his idea!'

The four of them strolled across the field, making their way through a wide gate and into another, this one filled with rows and rows of cars and vans, most of them with tables or stall set out in front of the vehicles.

Nessa was astonished; she'd never been to a car boot sale before, and although she knew what one was, this was all new to her. 'Good luck with the milk-churn hunt,' she said to the Porters as she and Mairi dawdled along. The farmer and his wife were clearly on a mission, and Nessa didn't think the old lady would be able to keep up with their fast pace once they'd spotted a likely looking stall.

'Fancy a hotdog and a cuppa before we get going?' Mairi asked. 'That's half the fun of coming here.'

'Go on, then.' Nessa didn't need her arm twisting; because of the upset with George earlier, the thought of breakfast had taken a back seat and she was now hungry.

Nessa queued to buy their food and drinks while Mairi found them a table.

'Mmm, I haven't had a hotdog in ages,' Nessa said around a mouthful of tasty sausage and sweet onions.

'Neither have I. Oh, I'm so pleased you moved in next door. When I'd heard Alys' cottage had been sold, I prayed it wasn't to someone who'd only use it for the odd weekend when the weather was nice.'

Nessa wasn't so sure her other neighbour felt the same way; in fact, she was certain he didn't, because he'd so succinctly informed her how he felt this morning. Oh well, one out of two…

'Do you fancy coming to lunch tomorrow? I'm having roast chicken and all the trimmings.' Nessa should have invited Mairi anyway, but she'd assumed having someone else there would frighten George off. Now it was a moot point, and Mairi could do with the company. So could Nessa herself, if she were honest, and the thought of sitting at her little table alone made her feel quite sad.

'That would be wonderful, dear. Thank you. I only ever have a roast dinner when I'm visiting my daughter; it's far too much trouble to go to just for myself.'

'You miss her, don't you?'

'Alison? Yes, I do. Very much. But her life is in Swansea, and mine is here, and that's the way it is.'

'Have you thought about selling up and moving closer to her?' Nessa asked.

'It has crossed my mind, but my home is in Applewell, and this is where my memories of Jim are. Besides, I don't like cities much. Although, as cities go, Swansea is a very nice one.'

'Do you ever get lonely?' It was a daft question – most elderly widows and widowers were, but Nessa was trying to gauge how much company Mairi needed; she didn't want to intrude if she had an active social life.

'Do *you*?' Mairi countered.

'Um, sometimes. Funnily enough, I didn't notice it as much when I lived in Bristol, but I was working, and days off were spent sleeping and catching up on chores. It was a faster pace of life.'

'Do you miss it?'

Nessa considered the question. 'Occasionally,' she admitted. 'Now all the excitement of moving and settling in is out of the way, I do think I need something to keep me busy.' An image of George's face this morning as he accused her of interfering leapt into her head and she thought again about what he'd said. Was she trying to keep herself occupied by being a busybody and sticking her nose in where it wasn't wanted, just to give her something to do?

She didn't think so. She hoped not. All she'd wanted to do was to make friends with him.

Another picture flashed across her mind – George standing on the beach staring out to sea, a brooding introspective figure, then the unreadable expression on his face when he had caught her watching him.

Was wanting to help him the only reason for her interest?

'Come on,' she said, jumping to her feet. 'Those doorknobs aren't going to buy themselves.'

And with that, Nessa firmly pushed George out of her mind.

But the problem was, she didn't for one minute believe he'd stay out.

Chapter 24

George

'What else was I to do?' George muttered under his breath as he changed his mind about going into the village, and stormed off in the direction of the cove instead. So what if he didn't buy a newspaper today? The only person who'd notice would be Sid, and if the viability of his shop depended on selling a copy of today's paper to a man who didn't even read it, then Sid was in dire straits.

George was about to push open the kissing gate leading to the field, but he hesitated as he considered what he'd just thought.

He didn't even read it.

So why did he buy it every day?

'Dad, Dad...' he groaned, thinking about how he used to go out every morning and pick up a paper for his father, bring it back to the bungalow and sit by the old man's bedside and read it to him. He missed that ritual with a fierceness which took his breath away, and suddenly the memory of the night his father died came into his mind.

It had been bitterly cold out, the moon a frozen crescent hanging in a clear sky. Breath had clouded around his head as he'd waited for the doctor to arrive, his father lying still and empty in the borrowed hospital bed.

He also remembered the pitying looks on the faces of the men who'd arrived to take away his father's body, and how they had struggled to manoeuvre the stretcher through the house and all the accumulated things.

He'd turned away then, unable to watch, only turning back when his father was gone. But his father – the man who'd taught him to dibble for crabs in the rock pools, who'd taught him how to replace a pane of glass, who'd taught him that all things had value and might one day come in handy – that man had gone long ago. For years he'd only been a shell of the man, of the father, he'd once been. And now the shell had gone, too.

What had George done, alone in the house for the very first time?

Once all the palaver had temporarily abated (there would be more, what with registering the death, arranging the funeral and then the ceremony itself) and the sun had risen, he'd walked into the village and had bought his father one final newspaper.

Except, it hadn't been the final one, had it?

There had been others. So many others that they now filled his hallway, having joined the ones he'd read to his father and had promised not to throw away – because you never knew when a couple of pages of the *Daily Trumpet* would come in handy.

But they never had come in handy.

They *might*, he knew they might. But so far, they hadn't. And he had no idea what he was going to do with them all.

He had no idea what he was going to do with any of it. Or with himself.

One thing was certain – he couldn't go on like this.

Blinking hard to force the unwelcome thoughts out of his head, George swung the gate open and strode through it, the path over the field drawing him relentlessly towards the one place that had always given him solace.

Why it had taken him so long to return to it, he didn't know. It had only ever held happy memories for him. But when he had, *she'd* been there. Watching him. Waving at him. Trying to be nice.

Was it so bad that she wanted to be neighbourly, to be friends, he asked himself, then he answered his own question. Of course it was! She'd discovered his... How should he refer to it? He refused to call it a secret, although that was precisely what it was. A shameful secret.

He *was* ashamed. Terribly. He knew his propensity to hang onto things wasn't healthy. He knew it was affecting his life in ways he probably couldn't begin to understand.

But this had been his way of living (of coping?) for so long, he was scared to change it.

Because if he did, he might not be able to cope at all.

George rounded the headland, the secret cove directly below, anticipation driving him forward.

But when it came into view, he stopped. There were people on the beach, a couple and two families, and he felt cheated. This was supposed to be the one place (apart from the bungalow) where he could be alone, yet the one time he'd visited it since he'd returned to Applewell, Nessa had intruded. And now these people. He knew it was nonsensical – of course all of Applewell knew about the cove – but he tended to think of it as his secret, and his alone.

It was symbolic in a way: first Nessa had found out about his hoarding, and soon the rest of the village would know how he chose to live his life.

But he hadn't chosen, had he? Not really. *It* appeared to have chosen *him*. No one in their right mind would want to live the way he did. Yet, there he was.

George watched the people on the sand below him; the couple, middle-aged and holding hands, the man scuffing up the sand with his trainers, the lady with bare feet, both of them smiling. The family nearest to them had three children, and the mother was sitting on a blanket, the children wore swimsuits and wielded buckets and spades with far greater enthusiasm than their harassed father. He recognised them as the Hargreaves, Lottie and Henry, and their offspring. The other family consisted of a dad with two children. George wondered whether the kids' mum had sent them off with their father to get the children out of her hair for a while. He remembered his mum doing the same thing, sending him and his dad out for the morning so she could get on with some housework.

George used to love those times. Just him and his father. 'Spending quality time,' they called it these days. George called it love.

God, how he missed his father, even now, after so long and after everything he'd had to do for him during those last few years of the old man's life. George regretted nothing. He'd do it again in a heartbeat.

With a heavy heart, he stared enviously at the children below. He'd been like them once, with his whole life ahead of him, full of sunshine and promise.

Now look at him.

His life was more than half over and what did he have to show for it – a house that didn't feel like a home, and a job he didn't care about. No wife, no children, no friends. Just stuff. Mountains of stuff.

Blinking back sudden tears (he didn't cry, ever; he'd learnt it didn't do any good) he came to a halt on the steep path, and stomped back across the cliffs. There was only one place left to him to go to, the one place that was both his sanctuary and his prison, and that was the bungalow.

George heard Nessa's car pull up. He knew it was hers from the sound of the engine, and because hers was the only vehicle to stop outside.

Unable to resist, he was drawn to the living-room window, regret riding him hard. Maybe he should have been a little less abrupt with her. Maybe he should have asked her nicely if she wouldn't mind keeping what she'd seen to herself. But he'd gone in all guns blazing and now he'd alienated her. He felt bad about that. Not so much what he'd said (she'd deserved it in a way – she *was* interfering), but he could have put his point across a little more gently. He wasn't rude or abrasive by nature, and it pained him to think she must believe he was. He just liked to keep himself to himself, that was all. What was wrong with that?

He watched her get out of the car, then help Mairi out, and he wondered where they'd been.

'It's a pity you couldn't find any knobs,' he heard Mairi say. 'Pins to Elephants might have some, or you could try the internet. My daughter says you can get anything you want on the internet.'

'I suppose,' Nessa said, and George had to practically press his ear to the glass to hear her. It was lucky he had his living-room window open, otherwise he wouldn't have been able to hear her at all.

'Are you sure you're OK?' Mairi said. 'You haven't been yourself today.'

George held his breath. It looked like Nessa hadn't shared their little contretemps with Mairi yet.

'I'm fine.' Nessa took a bag from the rear seat and slung it over her shoulder. 'Come on, let's get the kettle on and have a nice cup of tea.'

'Good idea. Are you going to do the rest of those cupboard doors?'

'I suppose I'll have to, unless I want to shell out for new ones. Although without knowing what paint George used and the exact colour...' Nessa's voice grew fainter as the pair of them made their way to Mairi's house and then they were gone.

George frowned. He thought for a while and he frowned some more.

Then he sneaked around the side of his bungalow, on pins in case Nessa emerged from Mairi's house, and made his way to the garage. He didn't dare open the old wooden doors at the front – he didn't know what might fall out and bury him – but he could get the side door open, and he proceeded to search.

It took him well over an hour, but when he emerged from the depths, he was holding several ceramic doorknobs. None of them were the same (goodness knows where they'd come from, but they'd been in a box in the garage ever since he could remember) and Nessa probably wouldn't want them anyway, considering he'd be the one giving them to her, and—

He took them into the living room and put them next to his computer.

It was enough, for the moment, that he'd found them. Whether he gave them to her, was something he'd have to think about.

Chapter 25

Nessa

So far, Sunday wasn't living up to its name – there wasn't a hint of sun in the sky, although the grey clouds suited Nessa's mood perfectly, as she glared at the offending cupboard door propped up against the cabinet.

It was early, and she resented being up at the crack of dawn when she had nothing to get up for. She used to be able to sleep on a penny and drop off instantly, but these days, since she'd retired and regular bedtimes had become the norm, sleep was ironically harder to come by.

Nessa blamed it on the quiet. She simply wasn't used to it yet. And when there was a noise, it wasn't anything normal like traffic, or aeroplanes, or people yelling. It was foxes barking, or cows mooing, or things going bump outside. Hedgehogs, she'd assumed, or perhaps those pesky foxes.

Sylvia didn't help. She kept mewing to go out. Or mewing to come back in. Nessa made a mental note to add 'get a cat flap installed' to her list of jobs. During the day it wasn't so bad because she could leave a window open. But not at night. Nessa liked to have her doors and windows firmly locked when it grew dark.

Her attention came back to the cupboards.

It was no good, she'd have to do something with them; they couldn't be left with one door a different colour to the rest and not even attached to the frame. It looked a proper mess, and Nessa disliked mess.

Which brought her back to thinking about George and his mess.

Once again, she briefly considered whether she might have got the wrong end of the stick and it was just his hallway that was in a state. Then she had another think about it and once again arrived at her first assumption — that George was a hoarder and the rest of the house was likely to be in the same condition.

It would explain a lot: his reluctance to answer the door; the way he acted on the rare occasion he did answer; in some ways it also explained his reluctance to socialise and not let anyone get too close.

Or maybe he was just a grumpy git who preferred his own company to that of anyone else's.

Nessa shook herself and returned to the problem of her kitchen. Without any paint, she wasn't able to tackle those pesky cupboards. The rest of the house was spick and span, she was on top of the laundry situation, and it was too soon to put the chicken in the oven. So at a loose end, she decided she might as well prepare the vegetables, but when she took the carrots out of the fridge, she hesitated.

Did she really want to cook lunch and eat it here, when George was next door? He'd probably be able to smell it cooking. He'd probably be able to hear her and Mairi, even though she planned to dine in the kitchen.

Would he think she'd been lying when she'd told him Mairi hadn't been invited, that it was only going to be the two of them? Or would he realise she'd only invited Mairi because he had turned her down? He might even think she'd done it out of spite.

Oh, hell, why was she letting him get to her like this?

It was none of his business who she invited into her house and for what reason. He'd had his chance and he passed. If she wanted to cook lunch for a lonely old lady, then she would.

The problem was, she thought George was equally lonely. More so, actually.

But because she didn't want to rub his nose in it, she returned the carrots to the fridge and came up with a different plan for lunch.

Chapter 26

George

Nessa was outside again, leading Mairi to her car, and he wondered where they might be going. That was two days in a row Nessa had taken Mairi somewhere and he was feeling a tad put out, with no idea why. It wasn't as though he wanted to go with them. Hell, he couldn't think of anything worse.

'Are you sure?' Mairi was asking in a querulous voice.

'I'm sure. I thought you might enjoy lunch out for a change. The chicken can keep.'

'Oh, I'm so looking forward to it, I haven't had a pub lunch in ages. And I'm so pleased you moved in next door.'

George strained to hear Nessa's reply because she had her back to him as she helped Mairi into the passenger seat of her car.

'Me, too. It'll make a nice change from cooking.' As she walked around to the driver's side, Nessa shot a swift glance at the bungalow and George shrank back.

He tried telling himself he was only looking out of the window so much because he now had something to look at due to all his neighbour's comings and goings. He also tried telling himself he only shrank back because she kept staring at him. Or rather, not at him (because she couldn't see through the nets), but in his general direction. Her continued curiosity made him uneasy, and that was why he couldn't help doing some staring of his own. It was a tit-for-tat kind of thing – if she didn't keep on looking at the bungalow, then he wouldn't feel compelled to look at *her* to see if she was looking at *him*.

He watched Nessa pull out of her drive in the car and tootle off down the lane.

Pub lunch, eh? So much for her inviting him to her house for a roast-chicken dinner. Despite what he'd said to her yesterday, he'd been rather hoping she might have repeated her invitation. He would have refused, of course, but she might have taken pity on him and popped around with a dinner on a plate.

It was wrong to hope, he knew. Not after what he'd said. He still felt incredibly bad about it. It was too late now; spoken words couldn't be unspoken. But there *was* something he could do to try to make amends.

He hadn't planned on going into the village today. This would be the third day he'd not gone in, the third day he'd not bought a newspaper. Sid must be ready to explode with curiosity. But he was running low on bread and milk, and his tinned-goods supply was looking rather dire because he'd been feeding himself out of the cupboard. So he could do with going shopping.

Unfortunately, he didn't want to. The thought of his private business having been touted all over the village made his blood run cold and he wasn't sure he could face anyone.

There was also the issue of him being out of routine. Midday was not the time he took his walk. It was too late for a morning one and too early for an afternoon one. He had been awake half the night and up at the crack of dawn though (so had Nessa – he'd seen a light on in her living room), so it did feel more like late afternoon according to his body clock.

Using this argument to justify a visit to the general store, George put his anorak on despite suspecting it was too warm to need it, and grabbed his fabric shopping bag.

Once upon a time he used to receive odd looks for having a reusable shopping bag; now though, they were regarded as sensible, ethical and moral. See, he thought as he slipped out of the front door, he wasn't totally daft, and neither was his old dad. People were far too keen to use things once, then throw them away. Not his dad, though. And not him.

Feeling slightly better, George made his way into the heart of Applewell, keeping his head up and his eyes straight ahead, looking neither left nor right.

He didn't see many people, just one woman pushing a pram and a man outside Sid's newsagents. There were a few more in the general store and he nodded to the ones he knew, the others he assumed were tourists. The tourists he ignored, but he shot an occasional glance in the direction of anyone he knew, trying to do so without being seen, to check if they were giving him odd looks.

No one took any notice of him whatsoever.

Maybe Nessa had been telling the truth when she claimed she'd not shared the details of the inside of his house with anyone.

After purchasing enough food to keep him going for a few days, he went into Pins to Elephants, ignoring the comical double-take from Tony who was restocking a shelf of wild birdseed.

'George, mate, how are you?'

'Fine, fine.' George made his way to the back of the shop where the paint was kept, hoping they stocked some in a similar colour.

He sensed Tony following, but he ignored him.

'Don't usually see you out and about at this time of day,' the man continued, much to George's annoyance. 'After anything in particular?'

George came to a halt in the painting-and-decorating section. 'Paint.'

'Doing some decorating, are you?'

'Hmm.'

'I'll leave you to it, shall I? Give us a shout if you need any help.'

George was glad Tony had taken the hint. He didn't want to chat. He never did, so why the owner of Pins to Elephants thought he might want to do so today was beyond him.

It took George five minutes of squinting and searching to admit he needed help. And another five minutes to ask for it.

Tony studied the piece of paper on which George had written the name of the manufacturer, the type of paint and the colour, and he sucked on his teeth and shook his head. 'Haven't got any of this on the shelves. They stopped making it, see.'

George reached out to take the piece of paper back, disappointment flooding through him. 'Thank you, anyway,' he said politely.

Tony whipped the paper away and waved it in the air. 'Didn't say I don't have any, did I?' he chortled, smirking. 'As it happens, I might have a tin or two in the stockroom. Got some oddments, see, but not enough for a proper shelf-full, and there's always new stock coming in that needs the space.' He frowned. 'I should sort out a sale section and get rid of it all. Half the time I don't know what's in that blimmin' room. I swear I've got stuff in there from the 1980s. Wouldn't be surprised if the paint you're after ain't from then.'

George wouldn't be, either.

'Hang on, I'll go and see what I can find. Keep an eye on the shop for us for a couple of minutes, will you?' And with that, Tony trotted off behind the counter and through a door marked 'staff only', leaving George alone on the shop floor.

What was he supposed to do now? Continue filling the shelf with birdseed? There were no other customers apart from him, but what if someone came in? Would Tony expect him to offer some assistance, or should he not say anything, but follow them around in case they fancied doing a spot of shoplifting?

George was still mulling over the problem when Tony reappeared several minutes later, brandishing two tins of paint.

'Result!' Tony crowed, plonking them down on the counter and slapping them with the palm of his hand. 'Is this what you're after?'

George hurried over and peered at them. 'Result' was an accurate turn of phrase, indeed. 'Thank you. How much do I owe you?'

'Give us a tenner and we'll call it quits.'

They cost more than that, George knew, from examining the tins on the shelves. 'That's far too cheap,' he pointed out.

'Nah, mate. As I said, it's about time I cleared all the old stuff out of the stockroom and had a sale. A fiver a tin is the sale price. You're doing me a favour.'

'I think it's the other way around,' George observed, pulling his wallet out of his pocket and handing Tony a ten-pound note.

'Happy painting,' Tony said. 'It's been in there a while though, so it might have gone off. Paint don't keep forever, so if you're not happy, bring it back and I'll give you a refund. Tell you what, come back anyway in a couple of days, because by then I'll have sorted through the old stuff and there might be something else you need on sale.'

'I shall,' George promised, picking up his paint and shifting a few things around so he could put the tins in the bottom of his shopping bag and not squash his food. He didn't think he'd be paying Tony another visit anytime soon – he had enough stuff of his own and he certainly didn't need any more.

Feeling pleased with himself, George stepped out of the shop and glanced across the road to the Busy Bumble as he did so. His attention was drawn to a familiar figure seated at a table by the window.

It was Nessa, and next to her was Mairi.

They seemed to be having a nice time. Mairi's face was wreathed in a smile, and Nessa's head was thrown back. She was laughing, and suddenly George wished he was sitting at that table laughing along with them. With *her*.

His good mood abruptly dissipated, and it was with a weary tread he returned to his bungalow. He'd leave the paint on her doorstep. There was nothing else he could do.

Chapter 27

Nessa

Mairi was a sweetheart and great fun to be with, but Nessa felt guilty for not enjoying herself as much as she should be doing. Which was why she was probably trying too hard and going slightly over the top – she didn't want Mairi to think she wasn't enjoying her company or the meal. The beef was delicious, but Nessa didn't have much of an appetite. She kept thinking about George; she'd had the feeling he'd wanted to accept her offer of Sunday lunch, and if she'd asked again, he may well have agreed. But then she'd seen the inside of his house and he'd been upset, and that was the end of that.

He was playing on her mind so much that at one point she'd almost imagined she'd seen him going into Pins to Elephants. Telling herself not to be so silly (it was the wrong time of day for George to be out and about), she turned her attention to Mairi, who was regaling her with a tale about one of John Porter's bulls and a naturist who'd thought the field was a safe place to do a spot of nude sunbathing.

'Are you all right, my dear?' Mairi asked, breaking into her thoughts.

'I'm fine, honestly.'

'If there's anything I can do, you will let me know, won't you?'

Nessa hesitated. 'It's George,' she said, as she pushed a glazed parsnip around her plate. 'I feel awful because I invited him to lunch.' It was kind of the truth, but not the real reason she was upset.

'I take it he refused?'

She nodded. 'I should have cooked anyway and taken a plate around to him.'

'Why?'

'Excuse me?'

'Why should you have done that?'

'Well… because… er…' Because she suspected he could do with a friend. She also suspected he mightn't do much in the way of cooking – she'd encountered lots of people who lived on their own and simply didn't bother making themselves proper meals. Yet she had no evidence to assume such a thing – he might be a top-notch cook for all she knew and regularly produced culinary delights for himself.

'He turned you down,' Mairi said firmly. 'It was his decision. You don't owe him anything. Anyway, I suspect he mightn't appreciate the gesture.' She gave Nessa a shrewd look and Nessa thought Mairi guessed it was George who had accused her of being interfering. Mairi was a smart cookie.

'I know, but…' How could Nessa say anything further without telling her what she'd seen beyond that open door? Although Mairi had already hinted George might be a hoarder, Nessa didn't want to be the one to confirm it. She'd meant what she'd said when she'd told George she wasn't going to tell anyone. It was his business; it was up to him to share it if he wished.

And maybe he was right – she had been a bit of a busybody, sticking her nose in and trying to make him be friends with her when he didn't want it.

But he'd looked so lonely and so desolate when she'd seen him on the beach, her heart had gone out to him. He'd also looked incredibly romantic, but she thought it best not to go there.

He was an enigma, was George Nightingale – on the surface he appeared to be a slightly conventional, stiff-upper-lip, rather stuffy and stand-offish man with a reputation for being a bit odd. But she'd seen another side of him and she was certainly intrigued by it. There was far more to George than meets the eye, she suspected. He was a bit Clark Kent – underneath clothes that a man from the 1950s would be proud of, and with his hair fashionably mussed, she knew a Superman was hiding.

OK, that might be taking things a little too far, she conceded. George Nightingale wasn't Superman. He was, however, quite attractive when you really looked at him and ignored his brusque demeanour. She wondered how many people (women?) had done that. She also wondered how many he'd allowed to get that close.

She tingled at the idea of getting close to him, of running her fingers through his grey-streaked hair, of stroking his forehead—

'He's like a feral cat, that one,' Mairi said, making Nessa jump.

Heat stole into her face as she realised where her wayward thoughts had been about to take her. Oh, dear, this simply wouldn't do at all.

'Who is?' she asked, stalling for time to try to get a grip on herself.

Mairi narrowed her eyes. 'We were just talking about George. Who else did you think I meant?'

'Sorry, I was miles away for a second.'

Another knowing look from the old lady. 'Not too far, I suspect. As I was saying,' she continued before Nessa had a chance to ask her to expand on the cryptic comment. 'He's like a stray dog. You've got to be patient and you've got to take baby steps. Too much too soon and you'll scare him off.'

'How do you know?' Nessa was curious. She placed her knife and fork neatly together on her plate and leant back in her chair.

'Because I've tried. Many of us have tried.' Mairi gestured around the pub, but Nessa had a feeling she meant Applewell as a whole. 'You've got further than anyone else.'

'I have?'

Mairi nodded gently. 'You have, so take comfort from that. But I will say one thing before we move on – he's got to want to let you into his life. You can't force your way in. And he may never be ready to do that. Excuse me, I need to visit the ladies.'

Nessa watched Mairi struggle to her feet and hobble towards the rear of the room, her thoughts on what she had just said. Hadn't Nessa thought the same thing herself? It was news to her, though, that others had tried to befriend him in the past and had failed. She took some comfort in knowing she was the one who'd made the most progress with him, but she also acknowledged the truth of Mairi's words – George would only accept help or friendship when he was ready.

'Are we ready for dessert?' Mairi said, returning to the table and sitting down.

'Why not? And a coffee to finish up?'

Mairi grinned. 'I think I'll have a splash of brandy in mine. Oh, and before you complain, I've already paid the bill.'

'Mairi!'

'Don't "Mairi" me. I wanted to do it. I don't have much to spend my money on these days, so this is my treat to say thank you for being a friend.'

Nessa shook her head. 'I suggested it, so I should pay.'

'Nonsense. And another thing; I've bought a meal for George. They're kindly packing it up for me as we speak. You can take it around to him later.'

Nessa's mouth fell open and her eyes widened.

'Just because he called you interfering doesn't mean you have to stop trying,' Mairi declared. 'Just remember, don't rush it.'

'Why don't you take it to him?' Nessa suggested, her mind reeling as she realised Mairi knew precisely who had suggested that she was interfering. 'After all, you bought it for him.'

'It's not my cupboard door he's painted,' Mairi retorted. 'And I don't think it's me who he wants to see – it's you.'

'I highly doubt that.'

'People are like animals – they lash out when they're scared.'

'You think George is scared?'

'Of course he is! We're all scared of something. You just have to show him he doesn't have to be scared of you.'

But what if I'm scared of him? Nessa thought. Never had a man crept under her skin like this one had. Not even her ex-husband.

As she tried to eat the berry pavlova which she wasn't sure she wanted now, she knew her heart was in more danger than it had ever been.

Chapter 28

George

They were back, Mairi and her new friend, and George wondered if they had enjoyed their lunch. He hadn't eaten his frozen roast beef ready-meal yet. For some reason his appetite had deserted him.

Nessa had once again opened the car's passenger door and helped Mairi extricate herself from the seat, and George was glad the old lady had someone she could call on, someone she could gossip to (as long as it wasn't about him). Yet part of him resented that that person was Nessa.

He felt excluded, like a third wheel in a relationship, no matter that he'd rejected each and every overture from both of them. And everyone else in Applewell, too. There'd been offers of help when he'd first returned to the village, but he'd thanked people politely and refused. His father had never wanted anyone near the bungalow, despite him not having been able to cope for a long time. He too, had been ashamed of the state of the inside of the house, George now realised, and it hadn't been half as bad then as it was now. A very private man was his father. Much like George. But was the desire for privacy driven by embarrassment?

George thought it might well be. He was trapped inside a cage of his own construction and he couldn't see any way out.

Various scenarios drifted through his mind. Should he go to the doctor? See a counsellor? A psychiatrist? Just leave and never come back?

The last option was the most favoured one, but he couldn't stomach what people would say about him after he'd gone. What he'd dearly like to do was to put the bungalow on the market and find a big city to lose himself in, where no one knew him and no one cared.

George froze as the thought he had had just sunk in. Did that mean someone *did* care? And not just to gossip? Genuinely cared?

He recalled all the times the shopkeepers and residents of Applewell had inquired how his father was, and had asked if there was anything they could do to help. He remembered the turn-out for his mother's funeral, and then his father's. The cards, the flowers, the way people would stop him in the street to offer their condolences.

He also remembered the way he'd politely brushed them off.

Coming back to Applewell hadn't been easy. He'd hated living here as a teenager. The name-calling, the pushing and shoving, the stealing of his dinner money, the bruises, had all left a mark. A bloody great big one. But what else could he do? His father had needed him.

It had been hard resigning from his job at the tax office, and it had been equally as hard leaving his city flat.

But the hardest thing had been returning to Applewell.

If he was honest, it wasn't the village or the people living in it which was the problem, because those children who had made his life a misery came from further afield (most of them) and they'd only caused him real issues in school. The problem was that Applewell reminded him of the way he used to feel when he was a child, and he didn't like it.

But he wasn't a child any longer. He needed to move past it.

It was a pity he didn't know how.

Oh, my God, Nessa was coming this way. She was heading up his drive with a wicker basket on her arm, the kind all the girls in school used to carry their ingredients in when they had cookery lessons. He hadn't seen one for years, but there was one in his parents' room on top of the wardrobe. At least, that was the last place he'd seen it.

He watched Nessa put the basket down on the step and he suddenly sprang into motion when she knocked.

This time he'd answer it. He'd thank her in person for whatever was in that basket. And he could give her the paint! It might go some way to making up for the way he'd spoken to her yesterday.

George hurried through the living room and into the hall, going as fast as he dared without running the risk of knocking anything over, and he yanked open his front door, a welcoming smile on his face and hope in his heart.

She was gone.

He heard her front door click shut and knew he'd taken too long. There had been too much in his way, as though the bungalow had conspired to hold him back, to keep him imprisoned within its walls.

Picking up the basket, George felt like crying.

Slowly, he made his way into the kitchen, placed the basket on that small area of uncluttered counter in front of the microwave, and lifted up the tea towel which hid its contents.

The basket contained a plate and a bowl wrapped in silver foil, plus two jars, one large and one small. It also contained a note.

George stared at the note for several long seconds before he took it out and read it.

Mairi bought you Sunday lunch. Please take the plates and basket back to the Busy Bumble next time you're in the village.

The handwriting was Nessa's, but the thought of gifting him a lunch had been Mairi's.

It took George a long time to remove the items from the basket, and even longer to decide he couldn't face eating any of it. The roast dinner looked delicious (it was beef, ironically, the same as the frozen meal he'd planned for today) and there was a large jar of rich gravy to go with it. Mairi had even ordered him a bowl filled with bright red berries and meringue. The smaller jar contained cream to pour over the top.

It was extremely thoughtful of her, and very generous.

And he felt incredibly ashamed that he wished it had been Nessa who had bought him lunch and not Mairi.

What kind of a person did that make him?

Unable to face either the food or his ingratitude a second longer, George emptied the plates and jars into the food bin outside, before carefully washing them and placing them back in the basket, with the folded tea towel on top.

Throughout the whole operation, he had tears in his eyes and a lead weight in his heart.

Now he could add wasting food to the list of things he hated about himself.

Chapter 29

George

Being unable to sleep was no fun. George was usually a fairly good sleeper, but on those nights where blessed oblivion eluded him, he tended to lie awake with his head filled with taunting thoughts.

Tonight was no exception. Memories kept running through his head like a series of nightmares on a loop. Why did no one ever have nice ideas in the middle of the night, he mused. It was as though every awful thing he'd done, imagined or prayed for, had come back to torment him. Apparently, it was quite common (he'd researched it online after one particularly disturbing night), but knowing other people experienced the same thing was no consolation.

There was one difference tonight from other sleepless nights, however – tonight he could hear noises.

Scratching, rustling noises.

Rat-like noises.

It was his greatest fear – not the rodents themselves, but what he'd have to do to get rid of them. Someone from the pest control department of the council would need to come out. And he'd have to let them into the house to assess the problem.

Reluctantly, he got up and went to investigate. Maybe he could frighten them off or something. He'd read they could be quite fearless when it came to humans, but he was sure if he made enough noise they'd give up and go back to where they'd come from. He was well aware the creatures liked enclosed spaces with lots of nesting material, and the dining room (he was sure that's where the noises were coming from) had nesting material aplenty.

Then there was the issue of how the little blighters had got in. That would have to be addressed too, once he'd moved his current unwelcome visitors on, because they'd undoubtedly be back. Crafty creatures were rats – they could enter a house through tiny cracks in the walls or through vents, or even, he'd read, through the spaces where cables and pipes ran. He was very careful never to leave food lying around and anything he threw away went into the lockable waste caddy outside, but they clearly liked what was in his dining room.

Steeling himself, he squeezed through his human version of a rat run as he edged through the hall towards the dining room. It was next to the kitchen and he always kept the door firmly shut. To be honest, he wasn't entirely sure he could open it now. Once, a couple of years ago, he'd heard a loud noise from inside and he'd been too scared at what he might find to take a look. The room was full to the ceiling anyway, and he couldn't get so much as a paperclip in there. That was when he'd begun to stack things in the kitchen. But now that room was also in danger of becoming a no-go area.

Hesitantly, he put his ear to the door and listened.

At first, he didn't hear anything, and he began to think maybe the noises he'd been hearing had come from outside, or from somewhere else in the house.

Ah, there it was again – scratching and an odd mewling noise.

Dear God, did rats mewl? Years ago he'd read a horror story by James Herbert and the subject matter had been rats. They'd mewled, he was certain of it.

The blood chilled in his veins and he shivered.

A loud thud from behind the door made him jump and he almost fell against a stack of flattened boxes before he caught his balance. Swearing, he put a hand on his chest, his heart thumping and he swallowed convulsively. Whatever was in there sounded bigger than a rat.

But that was impossible. Nothing larger, like a fox for instance, could possibly get in. Therefore it must be a rodent, and the sooner he scared it off, the better, before he had a whole family of the horrid pests setting up home in there.

George pressed down on the handle, took a deep breath and shoved with all his might.

The door moved a little, enough for George to get his head and one shoulder through, but no more.

It was also enough to see that the rat was no rat.

What was sitting atop a pile of plastic bags was Sylvia, Nessa's blue-eyed cat.

George yelled, the cat yowled, and by the time George had gathered his wits, Sylvia had disappeared.

In one way he was relieved to know there wasn't a rats' nest in his dining room, but in another he was disconcerted to realise he'd just frightened the little feline to death, and now he had to try to persuade it to come to him. He could hardly leave it in there in case it got stuck, although he supposed he could try leaving the door open and some food in the hall. It was bound to come out when it was hungry enough. Or it might get out the same way it got in. He reminded himself to check for the cat's entry method in the morning.

He was about to return to bed when he heard another loud thud from inside.

As he looked inside again, cricking his neck in the process and cursing under his breath, he saw that what had once been relative order in the room (his kind of order, that is) had dissolved into a room full of heaps and heaps of stuff, all jumbled together. It looked like there'd been a landslide.

'Here kitty, kitty,' he crooned, crouching down and shoving his arm through the door, then reaching out and clicking his fingers in an enticing manner. At least, he thought it was enticing – all the cat did was to meow in response whilst failing to show itself.

'Come to George, come on, kitty. Sylvia, I mean.'

Another plaintive meow, but he still was unable to see the cat and after fifteen minutes of him calling and the cat meowing he came to the conclusion either Sylvia was stuck or she wasn't coming out for *him*. He suspected the latter, but feared the former.

'Right,' he told her. 'I'm going to put some milk in a bowl and leave it out here. And when I've done that I'm going back to bed. You can stay in there all night if you want, I don't care.'

But he did care, and after he'd put the promised milk in the hall (he used one of the chipped saucers in the washing machine), he took himself back off to bed and lay there awake for the rest of the night, his ears straining for the sound of a cat's soft paws.

It was now morning, and the animal hadn't shown the slightest inclination to come out of the dining room. George stood in the hall, staring disconsolately at the untouched saucer of milk and pondering his next move.

Should he go into the village, buy some tinned cat food and try to tempt Sylvia out? Or should he force his way in through the jammed door and hunt the cat down – which was easier said than done considering what was blocking the doorway. There was also the possibility that his efforts to get her out might make the situation worse, because he was seriously beginning to suspect she was trapped. If he started moving things around (not that he had anywhere to move them to), the cat might become even more stuck or, God forbid, crushed. He'd seen and read enough online to know that people had died from being crushed by their own stuff. He'd tried to ignore the danger, but it wasn't easy to unread something once the words had entered the brain.

It would have to be the cat-food option first, he decided, but then he was faced with the problem of how long he should leave it before he was forced to take alternative action. Action that involved Nessa, who would be undeniably going frantic about her cat.

It wouldn't be fair on his neighbour to let her worry about the creature when he knew precisely where it was. He didn't think he could bear to hear Nessa calling and shaking the cat's bowl for hours on end.

That was it, then. He didn't have any choice – he had to tell Nessa.

And if it meant she had to enter the bungalow and see what he'd been reduced to, then so be it.

Taking a deep breath, George went to fetch Nessa.

Chapter 30

Nessa

This difficulty sleeping nonsense was getting to be a nuisance Nessa thought, as she dragged her weary body out of
bed and got dressed. She already knew, without having to
check, that Sylvia hadn't come home last night. If she had
done, the cat would either still be curled up in a ball at
the foot of the bed or patting Nessa's face with her paws
and demanding her breakfast.

Nessa checked anyway, even looking in the spare
bedroom in case the little madam had sneaked in there,
but there was no sign of her. The treats she'd left in the
kitchen before she'd gone to bed were untouched and the
flour she'd scattered on the windowsill below the open
kitchen window were devoid of tell-tale pawprints. She
hadn't wanted to leave a window open at night, but it was
only the top kitchen one, and if anyone had wanted to get
through it they'd have to be very thin and a contortionist
to boot. Or a cat.

It was too early to pop round to Mairi's to check if
Sylvia was there, and she certainly didn't intend to knock
on George's door again, so Nessa made a cup of tea and
prepared to wait until a more reasonable hour before she
disturbed the neighbours with her shouting.

Nessa vowed she'd make Sylvia wear a collar with a tracker on it the next time she allowed the cat out and she decided to have a look for one online.

She had just clicked on a suitable-looking website, when she heard a knock on her front door.

If that was Mairi, she was up early – but then again, if Sylvia had got into her house it wasn't any wonder. As well as being very vocal when she wanted something, the cat would tread all over you to get your attention, and Nessa defied anyone to sleep through that.

'I'm so sorry—' Nessa began, until she saw who was on her step and stopped. 'Oh, I thought you were Mairi.'

George was looking dishevelled, with a hint of stubble on his face and his hair sticking up as though he hadn't brushed it yet. He also had dark circles under his eyes and a wary expression in their depths.

'Your cat is in my bungalow,' he said, without any preamble. A good morning or a hello would have done. He evidently still wasn't happy with her, despite her (or rather Mairi's) gift of roast beef and pudding.

'I wondered where she'd got to,' Nessa said, silently questioning why he simply hadn't shooed Sylvia out or brought her with him.

'You'll have to come and get her. I think she's stuck.'

'Stuck where?'

'In my dining room.'

'Oh.' She stared at him for a second, while he stared back at her. A brief flash of acknowledgement passed between them.

'I'll come now.' She left him standing there on the doorstep while she went to put a pair of trainers on and fetch the cat treats she'd left out. After what he'd accused her of, she'd be damned if she'd ask him in.

He nodded at her when she stepped outside and she had the impression it was a resigned gesture. Without warning, she was filled with compassion. This couldn't be easy for him, inviting her into his house, even with her already knowing what she knew. She was about to see all of it, and not just the tiny peek through a doorway that she'd had two days ago.

'Thank you for lunch,' he said as they walked side by side down her driveway.

'You need to thank Mairi – it was her idea.'

'Yes, so you said in your note. Please thank her for me.'

'You should thank her yourself.' They turned onto his property and she knew there wasn't much time left to say what she wanted to say. 'I didn't tell her. About… you know… so don't think she gave you a roast beef dinner for any other reason than kindness.'

'Thank you.' He sounded as though he'd swallowed a marble.

'Did you enjoy it? Your lunch,' she added for clarification.

There was a tiny hesitation before he said, 'It was lovely. Very nice. Thank you.' He paused, his hand on his front door. Out of the corner of her eye, she saw him take a breath and lift his chin, before he pushed it open.

'I'd better go first,' he said, and she followed him inside.

Flippin' heck it was gloomy in here, was her first thought, swiftly followed by dismay as she saw the towering columns of paper either side of the narrow gap he was leading her through.

Immediately she felt hemmed in and claustrophobic, and she'd only been inside for a couple of seconds. God knows how George coped, having to live like this day in and day out. Maybe he liked it, but she didn't think so, as she was taken deeper into the depths of the bungalow and the walls of stuff seemed to close in on her. Terrified they might topple over and bury her beneath a pile of rubbish, Nessa's breathing quickened as she started to hyperventilate. She hated clutter at the best of times, and this degree of it made her break out in a cold sweat. How could anyone live like this, she thought in dismay.

Then from deep within, Nessa felt calm descend on her. George hadn't chosen to live this way, she knew. It had crept up on him, in the same way a glass of wine after work every evening for some people turned into two, then three, then a bottle. Or how skipping a meal because some unkind person called you fat might eventually lead to being fed through a tube in hospital. It wasn't a choice. It was a disorder.

Reaching for the inner strength she had displayed throughout her nursing career, Nessa focused on the issue at hand, namely trying to extricate her cat from George's dining room. Everything else could wait. It would have to wait, because he needed time to process having her in his home, time to come to terms with the fact she knew the full extent of his secret. He also needed time to realise she wasn't going to judge him. Or force anything on him or offer help from her or anyone else.

She simply had to trust he'd seek it out for himself when he was ready.

'She's in there.' George jerked his head at what she assumed was the dining-room door.

It was only open a crack, but through it she caught a glimpse of the chaos beyond and her heart sank.

If Sylvia was stuck, it was going to take a mammoth effort to free her; all this stuff would have to be shifted for a start and there wasn't anywhere to shift it to. Except to the skip, and she wasn't sure George would agree to that suggestion.

Nessa looked up at him as she squeezed past, her body brushing up against his in the impossibly narrow space. Her fear they might topple something over must have shown on her face and George slowly shook his head.

'I'm sorry,' he said.

'It's okay.' Nessa meant it. It *was* okay. She understood, she truly did, and she didn't judge him, or make any assumptions, or demands. She was simply there if he needed her.

As he gazed down at her (she hadn't realised he was so much taller than her), she saw shame and embarrassment reflected in his eyes and all she wanted to do was to put her arms around him and give him a hug. If ever there was a man in need of some love, it was George Nightingale.

She just wished she could be the person who gave it to him.

He stood back a little to give her room to crouch down and she was conscious of his eyes on her as she poured some treats into her hand and held it out. 'Sylvia, come to Mama,' she crooned. Immediately there was an answering feline chirrup and Nessa smiled. At least she knew where her cat was, even if it might take all day to get her out.

She looked over her shoulder at George, to smile reassuringly at him and what she saw on his face almost took her breath away. It was soft and filled with longing, but his face changed so swiftly when he realised she was looking at him, Nessa thought she must have imagined it. After all, the light in the hallway was dim; she was at an odd angle; he was relieved she was sorting the problem of her cat out, and he didn't have to... she came up with every excuse she could think of, but she still couldn't shake off the expression she had seen on his face.

Thoughtful, she turned her attention back to the meowing in the dining room and called again. 'Come on, poppet, come to Mama.' She felt a right idiot, but it was the way she usually spoke to her cat, and it was the best thing she could think of to persuade Sylvia to come out.

With an incredibly loud chirp, Sylvia suddenly appeared on the top of a tumbled pile of egg cartons. She jumped down with feline grace and perched on one of them, before sniffing the contents of Nessa's hand and proceeding to hoover up her treats.

Gradually, Nessa pulled her hand back, and Sylvia followed, until the animal was safely out of the dining room. Nessa scooped her up just as George leant over her and pulled the door shut.

She got to her feet, Sylvia in her arms. 'Thank you. I've been awake most of the night worrying where she was.'

'And I've been awake most of the night, knowing exactly where she was but not being able to get to her.'

Nessa smiled warmly at him. 'Do you know how she got in? I'm afraid she'll do it again now she knows how. Persistent little blighters are cats, especially this one.'

'I've no idea. I've been wracking my brains trying to think. There aren't any windows open in the dining room—' He uttered a sharp laugh. 'Not that it could be called a dining room... Not any more.' He began edging back down the hall towards the front door and Nessa followed him, trying not to let him see she was glancing at each room as they passed.

The kitchen was next door to the dining room and appeared to be equally as cluttered, although there was a small amount of floor space just inside the doorway between the fridge and a cupboard. There was what she thought might be a living room on the other side of the hall because she could see the arm of what might have been a sofa or a large chair, but the rest of the doors were firmly shut. She dreaded to think what lay beyond them. What she'd seen so far was bad enough.

George ushered her out, then pulled the front door closed. 'I'm going to take a look around the back,' he said. 'See if there's anything obvious.'

She watched him walk down the side of the bungalow towards the wooden gate which separated the front of his property from the back. It was positioned with the wall of the bungalow on one side and the wall of the garage on the other.

But before he reached the gate, he halted next to a window.

'This is how she got in,' he called to her. 'There's a small hole in the corner of one of the panes of glass, just above the windowsill.'

Nessa stepped forward to take a look. The hole might be small, but it was plenty big enough for a slim cat such as Sylvia to squeeze through. There was even a handy bin just below in case she'd needed any help reaching it and Nessa recognised it as similar to the bin she put her own food waste in. The little terror must have smelt something nice in there and when she wasn't able to get at it, decided to try her luck inside in case there was any more food in there.

'I've got some hardboard in the shed I can use to board it up,' George informed her.

Nessa guessed he probably had more than 'some', if the rest of the house was any indication.

'Do you know what caused it?' she asked, hoping he didn't think her cat had somehow broken the window.

'I think it might have been broken in the storm the other week. I found a decent-sized branch on the path, but I didn't think anything of it at the time.'

'At least it's not a big window, like the ones at the front,' she said, 'So it won't cost too much to replace.'

When Nessa saw George's face, she understood he didn't have the slightest intention of getting the window re-glazed and she knew the reasons why – there was no way he was going to let anyone else into his house. And even if he did, the glazier would be unable to reach the window.

She caught his defiant expression, and she knew she was right even before he replied, 'I can do any repairs myself.'

'I'm sure you can.' And he probably had a few sheets of glass in his shed, too, she thought, although how he was going to manage when the window in question was double-glazed, she simply didn't know.

'Thanks again,' she said, lifting Sylvia up. 'It can't have been easy.'

And that was where she left it. There was no point in her saying anything else. If George wanted help from her, he knew where to find her. She didn't intend to push her friendship onto him, but she did feel she'd made some progress.

Anything more was up to him.

She wished he'd get on with it though, because she really, really wanted to spend more time with him.

Chapter 31

George

George didn't know what to feel about having Nessa inside his house this morning. He actually didn't know what to feel about the last few weeks – not since she had moved in – although that was beside the point. He'd allowed someone inside, and they hadn't run away screaming.

He sensed Nessa had been shocked and he'd seen concern on her face, but he hadn't witnessed any pity or disgust.

He'd expected both.

Her acceptance had been a kind of revelation – if she could take him as she found him, then maybe others could, too?

Those were the thoughts circling through his head as he found some hardboard, cut it to size and nailed it over the broken window, after finding some suitably sized nails in an old jam jar in the shed. They were rusty, but they did the trick. Thank God the window frames were wooden and not uPVC, although they were in a bit of a state and would need replacing in the not-too-distant future – which obviously wasn't going to happen.

He then made a plan to work for the rest of the day on his accounts, because if he didn't, he was in grave danger of falling behind. He'd certainly done that over the past few days, as he had not been able to face looking at his computer, but today he felt a little better, and not so disconcerted or perturbed.

After a productive day where he'd spent more time staring at the screen than out of his window, George finally saved the files he'd been working on and decided to make himself some food.

By 'make' he meant warm something up in the microwave, as usual.

Which was why he was holding the defrosted beef-dinner ready meal from yesterday, and wondering if it was safe to pop it in the microwave after it had been out of the freezer for over a day, or whether he should heat up a tin of soup, when he heard a pounding on the door.

He knew who it would be (there was no one else it *could* be) and a smile spread across his lips as he hurried to open it.

It faded abruptly when he saw Nessa's expression.

'What's wrong?' he demanded, not bothering to try to hide his hallway from her this time.

'Have you seen Mairi today?' Nessa looked flustered and worried.

'No. I haven't been out of the house. And I haven't looked out of the window much, either,' he added for good measure.

'I'm worried – I haven't seen her since yesterday after-noon when we came back from lunch, and I've just popped round to check on her, but her curtains are closed.'

Hmm, that was odd; it was only just gone five o'clock. 'Maybe she's having a nap?'

Nessa shook her head. 'I don't think so, there's a bottle of milk on her step.'

George knew Mairi had a pint of John Porter's milk delivered every morning and it was very odd she hadn't taken it in. It must have curdled by now.

'Do you think she might have gone out for the day?' he suggested, knowing he was clutching at straws even as he said it.

'No, I don't think so. The milkman is here at the crack of dawn and even if she did go out early, she would have taken her milk in.' Nessa wrung her hands. 'I'm worried something awful has happened.'

George stepped outside and caught hold of her elbow. 'Come on, let's see if there's a window open or something.'

She smiled at him gratefully and the pair of them scurried down his drive and along the pavement.

Nessa was right – all the curtains on the front of Mairi's house were drawn.

Leaving Nessa to bang on the door, George hastened around the back and examined the windows. The kitchen curtains were also pulled to, and even though he cupped his hands against the glass, the tiny gap where they joined wasn't enough for him to see inside.

'Do you think we should call someone?' Nessa asked when he returned to the front of the house shaking his head.

'Do you have her daughter's phone number?'

'No, but even if I did it wouldn't be any use; Mairi said she's on holiday in Italy at the moment.'

The two of them stared at each other, then George said what they were both thinking. 'The police?'

'I don't see we have any other option. We can hardly break in.'

'I'll phone,' he offered. 'You stay here and keep trying.'

George dashed into the bungalow and made the phone call, adding they'd better send an ambulance, too. He didn't have a very good feeling about this, and he knew time was of the essence if Mairi had been taken ill or had had a fall. God forbid it would be anything worse.

The wait for the police seemed a long one, although it was probably no more than twenty minutes. Nessa kept knocking and calling out, but the inside of the cottage was ominously quiet, and eventually she simply stood there, her face creased with worry.

Looking at her face, George slipped an arm around her and drew her into him. 'I'm sure she'll be all right,' he murmured, praying it was true, but not necessarily believing it.

'I've seen too much of this,' she replied, biting her lip. 'I used to be a nurse in A and E.'

'Ah, I see.' She must have seen more than her fair share then, he thought, surprised he wasn't aware of it.

Then again, why would he be? He didn't know anything about this new neighbour of his, but he realised he very much wanted to get to know her better.

'Here they are,' he said, hearing an engine coming up the lane and spotting the familiar white, yellow and blue of a police vehicle.

He left Nessa to explain the situation, but he kept his arm around her thinking she might appreciate his physical and moral support.

But when Nessa made to enter Mairi's cottage after the police had gained entry, George released her, understanding somehow that she'd not be able to live with herself if she remained outside when there was something she could have done if—

He didn't complete his thought, hoping instead that they were in time.

'Stay back, my lovely,' one of the police officers said, trying to block Nessa's way as his colleague entered the house.

'I'm a nurse,' she told him. 'A trauma nurse.'

'I'm sorry, I still can't let you go in until we know what's what. Are you a relative?'

Nessa shook her head, her face crumpling, and George put his arms around her again, wishing he could take her distress away. It broke his heart to see her so upset.

'I'm sorry,' she spluttered, sobbing into his shirt, 'I'm not normally like this, but Mairi isn't a patient – she's a *friend*.'

'Let's wait and see what the medics say,' George said as the wailing of a siren was heard approaching in the distance.

It was a long wait, too long as far as George was concerned. They watched silently as one of the police officers came out to speak to the newly arrived para-medics, then accompany the medics inside.

They waited for ages for someone to come back out, and when someone did, it was to fetch a stretcher and some other equipment. All the while there was nothing either George or Nessa could do.

Eventually one of the officers came out to speak with them. 'We believe Mrs Edwards has suffered a stroke. She'll be taken to hospital in Aberystwyth. Do you know who her next of kin is?'

'She's got a daughter who lives in Swansea, but she's abroad at the moment. Can you tell me how Mairi is?'

The officer pulled a face. 'The hospital will be able to tell you more when she's assessed.'

'Can I go with her?'

'Best go in your own car,' George suggested, 'otherwise you'll have trouble getting back. I'll come with you,' he offered.

'Can you stay here? It's not that I don't want you to come with me,' Nessa added, as his face fell. 'It's just that someone needs to secure her house. The police have made a right mess of her front door. I'd hate for it to be burgled on top of what she's going through. And could you see to Sylvia? There's a spare key on a hook in my kitchen, and if you could lock up after yourself?'

'Of course.' Anything to help, he thought, although he dearly wanted to stay by Nessa's side – he had a feeling she'd need all the support she could get.

He held her tighter as Mairi was brought out on a stretcher, her frame small and shrunken, her face barely visible under a mask and all the tubes and wires.

Surprisingly, Nessa seemed to draw strength from the sight and George realised she must know precisely what all the equipment was and what it was used for.

The ambulance left first, then the police (after issuing pieces of paper with various details on), and Nessa sprang into action.

'Right,' she said, evidently relieved she was able to make herself useful. 'I'm going to pack a bag for her, then get off. They might not let me see her, but at least they can tell her I'm there.' Neither of them was prepared to face the fact that Mairi mightn't be in any condition to be aware of anything.

George followed her into the house and up the stairs; it didn't feel right going through Mairi's things and he guessed Mairi wouldn't be too keen on having a man rifling through her underwear drawer, so he left finding clean nighties to Nessa while he packed the old lady's slippers and hunted down a fresh bar of soap and any other toiletries he thought she might need.

Lastly, he popped the book on her bedside table into the bag, his face going pink as he caught Nessa staring at him. 'She might be able to read it,' he said defensively, 'and if she can't then someone could read it to her.'

Nessa stepped towards him, so close he could wrap his arms around her again if he wanted to (and he did want to – very much). 'That's so nice of you. Thank you.' With that, she stretched up, took his face in her hands, a palm on each cheek, and brought his head down.

Then she kissed him on the lips. Not a passionate kiss, but a kiss nevertheless, and a tingle shot through him from the top of his head to the ends of his toes.

Abruptly, she was gone, her feet hurrying down the stairs.

George followed, much more slowly, his fingers on his lips, his heart thumping.

He watched as Nessa threw Mairi's bag into the boot of her car and reversed onto the lane, his mind whirling, his thoughts a jumbled mess.

When she drove past Mairi's cottage, she wound her window down and leant across to shout, 'You're an incredibly nice man, George Nightingale, and I'm glad you're my neighbour.'

George was glad too, because that kiss, that one brief flutter of her lips on his had made him realise something – he was falling for Nessa Millbrook, and it was the best thing to have ever happened to him.

And possibly the worst.

Chapter 32

Nessa

'Ms Millbrook?'

Nessa leapt to her feet as a nurse called her name. 'That's me,' she cried, surprised she had enough energy to stagger to her feet, let alone jump up like a startled cat.

'Come through, Mrs Edwards has been asking for you, and the doctor would like a quick word.'

'She's conscious?' Relief swept over Nessa as she trotted after the nurse.

The nurse didn't answer her. Instead, she said, 'If you wait here, the doctor will have a chat, then you can go in and see her.' She pushed a door open and gestured for Nessa to enter.

Nessa knew better than to ask the nurse for clarification, so she did as she was told. For one thing, she was lucky the medical professionals were speaking to her at all considering she wasn't a relative, but she guessed Mairi must have given her permission. And for another, nurses were trained never to give medical assessments.

After a few minutes, a man walked in. 'My name is Doctor Khan and I have been treating Mrs Edwards.'

'How is she?' Nessa asked.

'She's had a cerebrovascular accident of the right hemisphere, which means—'

'She's had a stroke. I'm a nurse. Used to be. Retired now.'

'Then I don't need to explain.' He inclined his head in acknowledgement.

He didn't. He also didn't need to tell her the severity of the condition, but that was because he couldn't at this stage until a barrage of tests had been run, although he might give her an educated guess if she pushed him.

She decided not to. It was better to wait for any results, and she'd have a good idea for herself when she saw her friend.

So with that in mind, she asked to be taken to her, praying Mairi hadn't been too badly affected.

–

Nessa was exhausted. It was gone midnight when she got back to her little cottage and she was having trouble keeping her eyes open, despite the thoughts whirring around in her head at a hundred miles an hour.

She'd have a cup of tea then go to bed, but whether she'd be able to sleep was another matter. Poor Mairi. Life was going to be so much harder for the old lady from now on.

She'd barely clambered out of her car, when George appeared at her side.

'How is she?' he asked. 'I've been worried sick.'

'Aw, bless you.' She should have given George her mobile number, or asked for his, but it hadn't occurred to her at the time. 'I'll tell you inside, I'm gagging for a cuppa.' She locked the car and tottered up the driveway, her keys jangling in her hand. The noise reminded her of Mairi's damaged front door, and she glanced at it. It was neatly boarded up.

'I've arranged for someone to come out tomorrow to take a look at it,' George said, seeing the direction of her gaze. 'I suspect they'll have to replace it rather than repair it. And I've borrowed her backdoor key because you can't access the front.'

'Thank you. I don't know what I'd have done without you.'

'You'd have coped.' He sounded sure, but Nessa wasn't as confident. Blood and other bodily fluids she could deal with, but fixing broken front doors in the middle of the night wasn't her forte.

'You sit down and put your feet up while I make the tea. You look done in.'

'I am. I don't think I'm cut out for this any more.' A few months of retirement had softened her.

Whilst George busied himself in the kitchen, Nessa leant her head against the back of the sofa and closed her eyes. God, she was exhausted, physically and emotionally. She couldn't get the image out of her head of Mairi lying in the hospital bed looking old and shrunken, and so very frail. It broke her heart to think of her all alone on the ward they had been about to admit her to, and she wished she had been able to remain there to take care of her.

'Here you go.' George handed her a mug of steaming liquid and a plate containing two slices of hot buttered toast. He looked almost embarrassed as he said, 'I bet you haven't eaten anything since lunchtime.'

Nessa hadn't and, suddenly hungry, she bit into the toast with alacrity.

Halfway through the first piece, she said, 'Mairi has had a stroke in the right hemisphere of the brain, which means the left side of her body is affected. She doesn't seem to have a great deal of movement in her left arm or leg, but it's early days yet, and the hospital will spend the next few days assessing her.'

'Can she talk?'

'Yes, with some difficulty because the side of her mouth is drooping, but thankfully her type of stroke doesn't affect the speech and language centres in the brain. Mentally, she'll probably have other issues, though.' Nessa took another bite of her toast, chewing and swallowing before she said anything more.

George waited patiently, sitting on the sofa beside her, and she was abruptly glad she had someone to share the burden with.

After taking a sip of tea, she carried on. 'Mairi's main issue might be a change in personality, memory problems, an inability to judge situations or what is appropriate, to name but a few. It's difficult to say exactly at this stage.'

Nessa winced as she recalled sitting by Mairi's bedside earlier, holding her bony hand and trying to give whatever comfort she could to the frightened old lady, when the old lady in question had pulled her closer with surprising strength to say something totally inappropriate. It had involved Nessa and George and what they should be doing in bed. It made Nessa blush to think of it. That Mairi had echoed what Nessa herself had been dreaming of a few hours ago, was beside the point.

'She's not going to be returning to her cottage any time soon, is she?' George asked.

'I doubt it.' Nessa's eyes filled with tears and she struggled not to cry. It didn't matter that she'd witnessed this same scenario hundreds of times throughout the course of her nursing career, and each one made her incredibly sad. This time it was personal. Mairi would hate being in hospital. She would hate being in a nursing home even more. Her only hope was that she could go and live with her daughter in Swansea, but Nessa knew her daughter still worked, and she also knew Mairi might well need a great deal of care for the foreseeable future. Then there were all the inevitable hospital appointments, the physio, the blood tests...

George took the empty plate out of her hands. 'I'll tidy this up,' he said, 'then you should go to bed. There's nothing more to be done tonight.' He put a gentle hand on her shoulder. 'It was a good thing you're such a caring neighbour. Without you noticing something was wrong, she might—' He ground to a halt.

Nessa knew what he'd been about to say and she reached up to cover her hand with his and gave it a squeeze. He was right, she knew that, but she also couldn't stop thinking she should have noticed sooner. Time was of the essence when it came to limiting the damage a stroke caused and goodness knew how long it had been between Mairi suffering hers and getting to hospital. She could have succumbed just as she'd gone to bed last night and had been lying there until the police had arrived.

It didn't bear thinking about, so Nessa tried not to. She thought about what needed to be done instead. George had sorted out the front door, so she didn't need to bother about that, but she'd like to put fresh sheets on Mairi's bed and the one in her spare room in case her daughter had to stay overnight, and she needed to check on the dates of any food in the fridge, and...

Nessa closed her eyes, exhaustion deadening her body and making her mind sluggish.

The last thing she remembered was George stroking her hair and draping something warm and soft over her, before she drifted off to sleep.

Chapter 33

George

George could feel the smile on his face as he draped the throw around Nessa and tucked her in. He briefly considered whether to wake her and send her off to bed, but it didn't seem right, somehow. He didn't feel he knew her well enough; yet, at the same time, he felt he knew her better than anyone else.

Besides, he liked that she was comfortable enough to fall asleep in his presence – or was she simply so tired she'd have fallen asleep on a fence post? But there was the kiss she'd given him, although it had probably been a pity kiss (if there was such a thing) and he warned himself not to read too much into it.

His lips still tingled from it though – or so he imagined – and he couldn't get the feel of it out of his mind.

Immediately, he was ashamed; it wasn't right he should be imagining kissing her again when Mairi was lying desperately ill in hospital and Nessa was so worried. He didn't deserve to have a friend like her.

It was time he went home and gave himself a stern talking-to.

Before he went, he returned to the kitchen to check Nessa's back door was locked, but as he pressed down on the handle, his attention was caught by the cupboard door he'd painted. Nessa hadn't rehung it and it was propped up against the cupboard it belonged to. Even if he did say so himself, he'd made a decent enough job of the repaint and it looked good.

He wondered whether Nessa thought so, and if so, why had she left it where it was and not rehung it?

George thought back to the mess she'd made of the door when she'd attempted to paint it, and he guessed what the problem might be – she didn't think she was able to hang it herself. At least, that's what he hoped and that her failure to put it back where it belonged wasn't because she hated the colour and intended to change it.

Oh, what the hell, she could always ask him to take it back off again, he decided, and went searching for the cupboard's missing screws.

He found them in a little dish on the windowsill next to a screwdriver with a badly rounded head. No wonder she was worried about hanging it back on the frame if that was what she intended to use. He was surprised she'd managed to get the door off in the first place.

As quietly as he could, George slipped out of Nessa's house and into his own, returning a short while later carrying a crosshead screwdriver. He hadn't had to use it in ages, but he didn't mind a bit of DIY, and there was no point in having these tools if you didn't use them.

As soon as the thought crossed his mind, he saw the irony. There were very many things in his bungalow he didn't use…

There, the cupboard door was back on.

George tested it a few times, opening and closing it, making sure the bottom of the door was completely level with the bottom of the frame. It was perfect.

Standing back to admire his handiwork, he ran his eyes along the rest of the units. The new colour made the old ones look shabby and outdated, it looked as out of place as a butterfly among moths. The question was, should he return the new door to its mothlike state or transform the old ones into butterflies?

He laughed at himself, he was no good with words. He was far better with numbers. He would dearly love to be able to tell Nessa how he felt about her. Although he was terrified she wouldn't take him seriously, or would reject him completely, which would be much worse. The only thing he could do was to *show* her. Didn't they say actions spoke louder than words anyway?

Surprising himself, he started to systematically remove all the rest of the cupboard doors and take them into his garden. He might as well begin now. It might be nearly one o'clock in the morning, but he knew he'd not be able to sleep, and there was all that paint he'd bought just begging to be used. It would only go to waste if he didn't paint Nessa's cupboards. And if she hated the colour, he'd paint it another shade, and if she didn't like that one, he would keep on painting until she was happy.

George would do anything, absolutely anything, to make Nessa happy.

–

The sun had been up for three hours by the time he'd finished washing the brushes he'd used and had cleaned the little flecks of rust off the cupboard handles. He thought about the doorknobs he'd found after his long search through the contents of the shed and debated putting them on, but decided against it as going a step too far. Which was ridiculous, because stealing someone's cupboard doors, repainting them, and putting them back on again, was plenty far enough, and definitely more steps than he wanted to think about.

The doors had dried nicely – the chalk-based paint only took thirty minutes – but he wanted to give the paint as long as possible before he took them back to Nessa, so he decided to take a quick walk into the village. The bakery was open early and there was something he wanted from there.

Checking he didn't have any smudges of mint green on his hands or face, George quickly changed out of his old clothes and into his going-out and work things. He didn't intend doing any work today, but he didn't want anyone he might meet this morning to think he was letting standards slip.

Doreen in the bakery smiled pleasantly at him but didn't make conversation as she handed him a bag of Danish pastries and croissants, and he thought he'd got away without having to speak to anyone except to ask them for what he wanted, when he realised he needed milk.

Drat. The general store didn't open until eight o'clock. Did he want to hang around for twenty minutes or should he bite the bullet and pop into the newsagent?

He bit the bullet.

Sid was near the door, as though he'd been waiting for him.

The newsagent performed an exaggerated check of the clock which hung on the wall behind the counter. 'Flippin' heck! I thought I'd had an episode and missed a couple of hours.'

George smiled politely. Under the circumstances, Sid's joke wasn't funny. He did consider mentioning it, but didn't know whether Mairi would want her predicament spread all over the village. People would find out sooner or later – they always did in a small place like Applewell – but he wasn't going to be the one to tell them.

'I haven't seen you for a few days,' the newsagent continued. 'Are you all right, mate?'

George said, 'I'm fine, thanks,' like he always did when anyone asked how he was whether he felt fine or not, but today he was being perfectly honest. He *did* feel all right. Despite his concern about Mairi, he was feeling happier than he'd done in ages.

'Do you know, I think I am,' he added. And with that he slapped the correct change down on the counter, grabbed a bottle of milk and fled.

That was enough socialising for one day!

Chapter 34

Nessa

Nessa twitched and woke herself up with a start. It took her a moment to realise that she was lying on the sofa and a longer moment for the events of yesterday to come flooding back. She checked the time and couldn't believe she'd slept downstairs all night – or what had been left of it by the time she'd got back from the hospital and had then told George all about it.

She realised George must have put the throw on her before he left and she sent him her heartfelt thanks. Needing the loo, she saw to that first, then had a quick shower and brushed her teeth before inching her way back down the stairs – she was too old to spend the night on the sofa and for her body not to exact some revenge on her for the affront. Then she made her way into the kitchen for a cup of tea before she rang the hospital.

Bemused, she came to a halt as she entered the room. Not only was the newly painted cupboard door back on its hinges, but there were gaping holes where the rest of the kitchen doors should be. Someone (and she had a fairly good idea who) had stolen them. She smiled and shook her head.

She was still smiling when she heard a knock on the door just as the kettle was about to come to the boil.

'Morning, you,' she said softly, letting George in and wishing she'd put some make-up on and was wearing nicer clothes than the T-shirt and jeans she'd dragged on. It was silly, because he wasn't here to see *her* – he was here to ask how Mairi was.

'Have you had breakfast yet?' he asked, holding up a paper bag and waving at her. 'I've got us a selection of Danish pastries, or there are croissants, if you prefer.'

'Gimmee!' she cried, snatching the bag out of his hand and inhaling the sweet aroma emanating from it. 'I'm starving.' She got out a large plate and slid the pastries onto it. 'I haven't phoned the hospital yet, but when I do, I don't expect them to tell me much. We're better off going to see her this afternoon.'

'You want me to come with you?'

Nessa noticed he was dressed in what she privately thought of as his old-movie-star clothes. He reminded her of an actor from yesteryear – not anyone in particular, although he had a bit of James Stewart about him in that he wasn't classically in-your-face handsome, but quietly good-looking. He was as softly spoken as the actor had been, too. And he had a similar hairstyle – when it wasn't ruffled from the wind.

She vividly recalled the sight of him staring moodily out to sea that day on the beach. He'd been more of a glowering Clark Gable then, but without the moustache.

Nessa turned to face him. 'Yes, I would like you to come. If you want to, that is. No obligation.'

'I would like to. Thank you for asking me, you're very kind.'

He'd resorted to being rather formal again which she guessed was his default setting when he was faced with a situation he wasn't sure how to deal with. What had she

221

said to make him react that way — had it been the 'no obligation' part? Did he think she was only asking him out of politeness?

'Good,' she replied warmly. 'I really, really want you to come with me.'

He gave an evaluating look, as though he was trying to work out if there was an undercurrent to her words, and she concluded he was the type of person who would always second-guess what was being said. She decided she needed to clarify a few things to help him to be at ease a little.

'Not because I need you to accompany me — I'm very much at home on a ward.' She laughed a little at this point, her nerves showing. 'And not because I think Mairi would love to see you — although she most certainly would.' Nessa paused. 'I want you there because I like you. I want to get to know you better, to spend more time with you.' She knew she was blushing, but she couldn't help it.

There, she'd laid it out for him. Surely after the kiss she'd given him yesterday, and this speech today, he would realise she liked him. Really liked him.

Evidently not, because he continued to stare at her as though she was speaking a foreign language, or as though she was some kind of puzzle he had to solve.

With a frustrated sigh, she walked across the kitchen, noting the way his eyes widened and his lips parted slightly as she drew nearer, until she was standing so close their bodies were almost touching.

Suddenly they *were* touching, as she wove her arms around his neck and reached up to kiss him, her lips meeting his.

He froze for the briefest of moments and Nessa was terrified she'd done the wrong thing and he didn't want this, but then his arms came around her, crushing her to him, and he let out a small groan.

Tentative and uncertain at first, he swiftly deepened the kiss, his mouth claiming hers with a ferocity that left her gasping.

When he finally released her, there was such wonder in his eyes that Nessa felt like crying. She touched a finger to his lips and he kissed it, his gaze never leaving hers.

'Well,' she said finally, not knowing what else to say.

'Well,' he repeated, his expression soft and filled with adoration, and her heart melted.

She wanted nothing more than to whisk him off to bed, but she'd been forward enough already. It was best to let this wonderful kiss simmer.

Suddenly embarrassed, Nessa stepped away from him and flicked the switch on the kettle. 'Tea?'

'Please.'

'Am I right in assuming you are my cupboard-door thief?' She kept her tone light and teasing.

'I hope you don't mind.'

Oh dear, he'd gone all formal again. Breaking down George's barriers was clearly going to take more than a kiss or two. She hadn't truly expected anything else – a lifetime of reticence wasn't going to be easily surmounted.

But she had been delightfully surprised at how expert a kisser he was. He'd done that before, quite a few times she suspected, and she briefly wondered what else he was expert at, before she brought her mind back to where it should be for nine o'clock on a Tuesday morning.

'I think it's a lovely thing to do,' she told him, running a hand across the smooth surface of the remaining door and wishing it was his chest she was stroking.

Good grief! What had got into her? She never behaved like this. Mind you, it was aeons since she had felt close enough emotionally to a man to behave in such a way. It was rather liberating and quite scary. She'd had a few relationships since her marriage had failed, but they'd all fallen by the wayside because of the demands of her job. One fella had accused her of caring more about her work than about him. He'd been right.

'Better than buying new,' he muttered. 'There's nothing wrong with them.'

'Except for the colour. They were looking awfully dated.'

'Is the green OK?'

'To be honest, I didn't like it at first. But it goes, doesn't it? With the curtains, I mean. And it brightens and lifts the whole kitchen.'

George's expression was blank. 'It was the only tin of furniture paint I could lay my hands on.'

Nessa laughed. 'You mean to tell me, this wasn't a carefully thought out colour scheme?'

'No.' He suddenly looked worried. 'Should it have been?'

'Not at all. The colour is perfect.'

She saw his shoulders relax as some of the tension leached out of them. 'I was a bit concerned,' he said. 'I bought some more, and there's plenty left over after painting all the doors so if you ever need any...' He trailed off. 'Would you like me to bring the tin round? I can go and fetch it right now.'

'No need. Not unless you want it out of your house.' She saw by his face he was conflicted, and he shuffled from foot to foot. 'It's not easy for you to let go of things, is it?' she said gently.

George looked at the floor tiles and continued to shuffle.

'That's OK. You don't have to get rid of anything you don't want to. If you'd like to keep the paint at your house, then keep it. It might come in handy.'

'Stop.'

'I'm sorry.' She didn't want to upset him, that was the last thing she wanted, and it was none of her business if he lived surrounded by clutter. Who was she to tell him to throw it out?

'That's what started it – keeping things because they might come in handy.' He was forcing the words through stiff lips.

Nessa knew better than to say anything in response; if he wanted to confide in her he would. She placed a mug of tea on the table and gestured for him to sit down, before taking a seat and wrapping her hands around her own mug. The pastries and croissants sat on a plate in the centre, untouched and ignored.

George sat down, his hands in his lap, his attention on the mug. 'It was my father who started it really. He always used to say "waste not, want not" to me. He never threw anything out when I was growing up. Mind you, in those days we didn't have much to throw away, not like today. If you went to the butcher, your meat was wrapped in greaseproof paper, not plastic, and my mother used to wipe it down and reuse it.' He uttered a small laugh. 'I don't suppose it was very hygienic.'

He unclasped his hands from where they'd been resting in his lap, picked up his tea and took a sip.

'I left when I was eighteen – went to university – and didn't come back. Not to live, not then. I used to visit, and every time I did there was more stuff in the house and garage. Especially by the time my mother became ill. So much stuff—'

He stopped and Nessa wanted to gather him to her and make it all better, but she held back.

Another sip, then he was ready to go on.

'When she died, my father refused to get rid of anything of hers. It's still in there – her clothes, her medicines, her comb. Even her toothbrush.'

Nessa bit her lip, the sting of tears sharp behind her eyes.

'I had to give up my job to look after him. When my mother went, there was no one else. He was a good man, my father. A gentle man. Kept himself to himself. What else could I do? I couldn't allow him to go into a nursing home – he'd have hated it. So I packed in my job, became a freelance accountant and moved back to Applewell to look after him. I've been here ever since.' George seemed to be looking for approval, or confirmation he had done the right thing.

'You can only do what you can do,' she said to him, biting back tears. 'I'm sure you did your best.'

'Did I, though?'

'What makes you think you didn't?' She wasn't trying to play the role of a psychiatrist – she genuinely wanted to know.

He shrugged. 'He died anyway.'

'George...' She reached across the table and her hand hovered in mid-air before she withdrew it. 'He was always going to die. You know that. But I bet he was happier when he was alive because you were with him and he was able to stay in his own home.'

'That bungalow is not a home. It's a mausoleum. I should have insisted he got rid of my mother's things. *I* should have got rid of them. And then his.' He finally met her gaze. 'Now look at me.'

'It's not too late, you know. It's never too late. I can help, if you like.'

'I'm not sure.' His expression was tortured, and she guessed how hard it must be for him to even think about removing all those items from the house, let alone actually doing it.

'You've got to want to do it for *you*,' she continued. 'Not because other people think you need to.'

'Do you think I need to?'

'That's not what I said.'

'Do you?' he insisted.

Nessa took her time answering him, choosing her words carefully. 'I don't believe you are happy. Being unable to let go of physical things could either be a cause or a symptom of your unhappiness. Probably both. It isn't easy either, when you're essentially right.'

He raised his eyebrows, and she carried on.

'Look at my kitchen cupboards – I was all for buying new. If it wasn't for the paint you found, and your kind-ness, I probably would have thrown the old ones out. "Waste not, want not" is a mantra more of us should adopt. You've just taken it to an extreme, that's all.'

His laugh was bitter. 'I suppose that's one way of looking at it.'

'Do you want to get rid of some of the stuff?' Nessa asked.

He pulled a face. 'I should, I know I should, but it's my history. It's who I am.'

'It's only part of who you are. It doesn't have to define you.'

227

George didn't look convinced. 'It's been me for so long…'

'It doesn't have to be you for ever. When you're ready, truly ready, I'll help if that's what you want. Please don't feel I'm pressuring you – I'm not. I don't care if you live in a mansion or a cardboard box. I just want you to be happy.'

Nessa watched as his face lit up, slowly, as though a dimmer switch was gradually being turned to maximum. 'That's the nicest thing anyone has ever said to me,' he whispered.

'Isn't that what your parents wanted? Isn't it what everyone wants for the people they care about?' Nessa reached for him and this time she clasped his hand tightly in hers and he squeezed back. 'When you're ready,' she repeated. 'You don't have to do it alone. I'll be with you every step of the way.'

He looked up at the ceiling and blinked hard, before dropping his gaze to hers. 'Can I think about it?'

God, she hoped he didn't take too long – the sooner he freed himself from the shackles of his past, the sooner he could face his future. One in which Nessa sincerely hoped she would be a part.

Chapter 35

George

'Thank God you had the presence of mind to grab the key out of Mairi's back door,' Nessa said as George dropped into the passenger seat of her car later that day and snapped the seat belt into place.

'I assumed Mairi's daughter would have a key to the front door, but not the back,' he replied logically, and considering the front door was boarded up, no one was getting in the cottage that way until it had been repaired. A bloke had come out this morning to take a look at it and had shaken his head and drawn a long breath in through his teeth, before announcing the door would need to be replaced. George had told him to go ahead – he'd pay for it himself if Mairi's insurance didn't cough up.

'I wonder if the hospital has been able to get in touch with her daughter?' Nessa mused, pulling onto the lane.

George studied her as she drove, noting her quick, decisive movements, and he thought about the car in his garage. It had been there a while. He bet it wouldn't start. He'd driven the Corsa from Liverpool to Applewell, and had used it to ferry his father back and forth to the hospital and the doctor's surgery. But when his father had died, George had driven the car into the garage with difficulty and a great deal of shifting and moving of assorted things, and there it had remained ever since.

'Do you think driving is like riding a bicycle?' he asked.

'Hmm? Oh, er, I suppose so. Why?'

'I've got a car.'

'You have?' She looked surprised, as well she might be.

'It's in the garage. I haven't driven it for years. I haven't been *in* a car for years, except for last night.'

'How do you manage?'

'If I absolutely have to go anywhere further afield, I take a bus or a taxi. Or walk. I've got everything I need in Applewell.' George considered what he'd just said and realised it was the truth. Especially now Nessa lived in it. But that wasn't what he'd meant. 'I work from home, and what I can't buy in the village, I have delivered. It's rare, though, and it only happens now and again, like when I have to update my computer.'

'Don't you have a spare or two lurking around your bungalow?'

George inhaled sharply before realising she was teasing him. Nice teasing, not the nasty variety he'd endured in his youth. It was good she could talk about it, he decided. It would help him immensely if she did, too.

'As a matter of fact, I have. But they're all old and slow. Which is why they needed to be updated.'

'You could sell them for parts,' she suggested, winding her window down and letting the wind ruffle her hair.

'I don't think so.'

Her face fell and he knew what she was thinking. 'It's not that I want to hang on to them per se,' he explained, although he did (the thought of them not being in his bungalow any more gave him goosebumps). 'There is still client information on them. I've put each one back to factory settings, but I wouldn't like them to fall into the wrong hands just in case.'

'I see.' Nessa's expression cleared. 'You could remove the hard drive and give the casing away,' she suggested, and it was his turn to feel a little despondent. Trust her to come up with a solution.

George suddenly realised he might not be as keen to start emptying the bungalow of its contents as he'd thought.

Yet if he wanted to move on – and he did, so much so it hurt to think about it – he knew Nessa was right. So many possessions were holding him back and he'd already taken the first steps by breaking himself of the habit of buying a newspaper every day. He still had to gift Nessa the rest of the paint and he *would* definitely give it to her. Just not today. Tomorrow, maybe. And he'd already given her one of his sweet tins to put cake in, so he was definitely making progress.

Baby steps, he told himself. He didn't want to risk trying to do too much too soon and being overwhelmed at the enormity of the task. He had found pleasure though in being able to use the green paint he'd already got, even if he hadn't had enough of it to complete the job. Donating the sweet tin for Nessa to use for cakes and things hadn't been quite the same, because he thought he'd get it back, hopefully filled with baked goods, so that didn't count.

Loath to get rid (he disliked the term intensely, but 'throw away' was worse) of anything in his house, he seriously didn't know how he should begin. Everything held a memory… wait, that wasn't strictly true. The egg boxes were of no emotional value whatsoever, apart from their intrinsic value of being useful to put eggs in, or maybe for other purposes such as soundproofing or insulation. They didn't *mean* anything to him – so why was he so reluctant to let them go?

He was brought out of his thoughts by the sign indicating they'd arrived at the hospital. It took them a while to find a parking space and George was glad to get out of the car. He hadn't sat in such a confined space for a long time – which was incongruous since his whole bungalow was a confined space – and he was feeling rather restless and angsty. It might also be because this was the hospital where he'd brought his father numerous times. Or maybe it was because he'd been sitting a foot away from Nessa and being so near to her was extremely unnerving. He wasn't used to wanting to kiss someone and he'd really wanted to kiss Nessa.

He still did, but a hospital car park wasn't the place to do it, especially with Mairi on both of their minds.

Mairi was so tiny she looked doll-like in the white bed, and George was dismayed. She'd been so vibrant, so alive. Now, though, she was frail and sallow, and it was heartbreaking to see the number of tubes and wires she was connected to. But he took comfort in the way her eyes lit up when she saw them enter the ward; there was hope for her yet.

'Nessa,' she whispered, and Nessa leant over her to give her a kiss on the cheek. George wanted to do the same, but he didn't feel he knew her well enough – to his shame. He'd lived a couple of doors away from her for years; he should have been a better neighbour.

At a loss to know what to say, he watched Nessa pick up the clipboard from the bottom of the bed and read the attached paperwork. 'Anything?'

'Not a lot. Just general stats about blood pressure, medication given, bowel movements—'

George held up a hand. 'I don't think I need to hear that, do you, Mairi? One's bodily functions should remain private.'

Mairi's mouth moved, but George couldn't hear, so he moved closer and bent down.

When he finally understood what she was saying, he shot upright in panic. Did old ladies really say things like that?

Nessa saw and she drew him to one side. 'Did she say something inappropriate?'

George, eyes wide, nodded. He hoped Nessa didn't ask him what it was.

'That's a result of the stroke. It can cause behavioural changes.' She winced. 'Depending on the severity of the damage, they might be permanent. It'll make visiting hours interesting.'

George blew out a breath. It certainly would.

He just hoped sometime in the future he'd be able to do what Mairi had told him he should; Nessa was already in his heart, he'd like her to be in his bed, too.

Chapter 36

Nessa

Whatever Mairi had said to George must have spooked him, because he'd hastened off to find the ward sister and had only returned when visiting was almost over. She watched him approach Mairi to say goodbye and he did so with as much caution as a mouse would display if there was a cat in the vicinity. She was tempted to ask, but thought better of it. She didn't want to scare him more than he was already. He was making good progress – she didn't intend to jeopardise it.

Instead, they drove home in thoughtful silence after George had informed her Mairi's daughter would be arriving back in the UK today, and the sister had said Mairi was facing months of rehabilitation. It was a sobering and sad thought, and Nessa's heart went out to her friend. If she could do anything to help her, she would.

She parked the car on her drive and debated what she was going to do for the rest of the day.

George made her mind up for her when he got out of the car and said, 'If you're not too busy or too tired, I need some fresh air. Do you fancy going for a walk?'

It was a warm and sunny day, and she could do with stretching her legs and blowing away the cobwebs. She didn't fancy reading or baking, and there was very little housework to be done. She'd only be sitting around worrying about Mairi.

'What a good idea. How about a picnic while we're at it? I don't know about you, but I didn't fancy much in the way of lunch before we went to the hospital, but I'm feeling a little better about things now I've seen Mairi for myself.' She wasn't, but there was no point in letting George know her fears for the old lady's future, especially since the hospital wasn't being very forthcoming about her prognosis.

'That would be wonderful.' He grimaced. 'I haven't got a great deal of food in my fridge, though.'

'I've got plenty, if you don't mind sandwiches and pork pies. I could do some cheese and pickle ones, and I've got a slab of Battenburg cake, if you're interested.'

'I can provide a basket. I'll use the one from the Busy Bumble – I haven't had a chance to take it back yet.' He gave her a wry smile. 'There is a proper picnic basket in the dining room; it's got everything you can think of in it, like a little salt-and-pepper shaker, a bottle opener and everything. It's just a pity I can't get at it.'

They shared a rueful look.

'We'll use the one belonging to the pub for the time being,' Nessa said, 'but how about we have a go at digging out the other one ready for next time?'

She hoped he'd get the subtext – that there was going to be a next time. That this wasn't a one-off. There would be other occasions when they would share a picnic. Quiet excitement filled her. She wasn't simply being nice or neighbourly – she enjoyed being with him.

He must have understood, because he walked around to the driver's side and gave her a kiss. Not a cheek job, or a swift peck, but a proper in-depth, toe-curling, breath-stealing kiss.

When he released her, Nessa's eyes were wide and her face was hot, and she guessed she must be blushing. She also had trouble catching her breath.

My God, this man was delectable. She could spend the rest of the day kissing him, and from the hunger in his eyes she guessed he'd be up for that, too.

'I'd best get that picnic made,' she said, to break the tension simmering between them.

'I suppose you'd best,' he replied, but as she watched him make his way to his own house, what she really wanted to do was to whisk him off to bed.

A short while later they were making their way along the path, across the fields leading to the cliffs. Although familiar, today the walk felt new, and Nessa guessed it was because she wasn't alone. George was by her side, the ever-present breeze ruffling his hair, the basket in his hand. Gone was his more formal attire and in its place was a shirt with the sleeves rolled up, jeans and boots. It suited him.

Nessa hugged the blanket she was carrying to her and wondered how he'd react if she held his hand.

Although he had been the one to suggest a walk and he hadn't objected to being kissed (in fact he'd initiated one or two of them), she wasn't sure how to view this little outing. Was it a date? Or a casual stroll between friends?

There was only one way to find out.

With nervous fingers, she reached for his hand and entwined them through his.

Then they were walking hand in hand like a couple of lovers and it felt so good Nessa wanted to shout about it from the tops of those cliffs they were heading towards.

Like a gentleman, as soon as the track across the fields joined with the rough coastal path, George stepped around her, putting himself on the side nearest the drop, before taking her hand once more, although they were forced to walk single file down the rocky bit leading towards their cove. George went first and she simply knew that it was to break her fall in case she slipped, and Nessa felt as though he was looking after her.

She hadn't felt that way since before her short-lived marriage had ended – she'd always been the one to do the looking after. It came with the job, she supposed, but it was also part of her nature, yet it felt incredibly good to have someone looking out for her for a change.

Maybe that was what had been lacking in George's life? It could be he needed to have someone to look after. Someone to love. She hoped it would be her. In time. Because she was halfway to loving him already and she wasn't sure how she'd manage if he never felt the same way about her.

'When we get back, I'll hang your cupboard doors back on. If you want me to, that is. They'll be well and truly dry by then.' George gave her hand a squeeze. He'd taken it again when they reached the bottom of the path and they were now walking across the sand.

'That would be wonderful, and as a thank you I'll make us a spot of supper. It won't be much because we're about to have a picnic, but I'm sure I can come up with something tasty.'

'You're intent on feeding me, aren't you? Do I look like I need feeding up?'

'Frankly, yes.'

'Are you calling me skinny?' He stopped and took the blanket from her, shaking it out and spreading it on the sand.

'Not at all. You're slim, but not skinny. What I mean is, you'd probably appreciate someone else cooking for you for a change.'

'What about you? You live alone, too. Don't you get fed up with having to make all your own meals?'

Nessa sank onto the blanket and slipped off her trainers. George followed, wrestling with his boots. 'I'm used to it,' she said. 'Even when I was married, I did all the cooking.'

'You were married?'

She nodded. 'I was in my twenties and it didn't last long.'

'Has there been anyone special since?'

It would be an easy question to dodge or gloss over, but Nessa decided to put her cards on the table. She was too old to play games, too old to mess about when it came to relationships. If this one was going somewhere, then she wanted to know about it. If they were destined to be nothing more than friends, then she wanted to know that, too. When she'd moved to Applewell the last thing she'd been looking for was love. But she'd found it, and the sooner she dealt with it the better.

'Not until now,' she replied quietly.

George was silent. He stared out to sea for a long, long time. Long enough so Nessa was sure she had her answer.

Then he said, with his eyes still focused on the restless water, 'I feel the same way. You are special, Nessa Mill-brook, and I want to get to know you much, much better.'

Nessa worried at her lip, a smile threatening to break free. 'So, then… is this a date?'

'Do you want it to be?'

238

She couldn't read anything from his expression, but she heard the hope and the fear in his voice. 'Oh yes, very much so.'

'Then, that's what it is.' And with that, he turned to her, gathered her in his arms and kissed her until she forgot all about their picnic.

Chapter 37

George

George knew about dating, in that he'd read about it and heard it discussed on the radio. He didn't have much in the way of first-hand experience, and hadn't for a good many years. He speculated whether it had changed all that much since he'd last asked a woman out.

He wasn't sure if the protocol was the same. These days one heard about women asking men on dates. In his day that hadn't happened. Or if it had, then not to him. It didn't feel right, anyway. Call him old-fashioned, but he believed the man should do the asking, and he wondered when he'd suggested a walk yesterday, whether he'd actually asked her out on a date and hadn't realised it.

The picnic on the beach and the kissing which had followed had certainly felt like a date. George's cheeks glowed when he thought about how soft Nessa's lips had been, and how delicious she'd tasted. How good she'd felt when he'd crushed her to his chest and wrapped his arms around her. How she'd wound her hands around the back of his neck, and how warm her breath had been as it fanned his cheek.

Sleep last night had been a long time coming as he had relived the day over and over again in his mind, savouring every second of it. Every time he thought about Nessa (which was more or less continually), his heart beat faster and his tummy turned over. He was scared, exhilarated and hopeful all in the same measure.

These past couple of days had been a roller coaster; one that he didn't want to get off. He'd never felt so alive as he did right now. Nessa had brought the sun into his previously gloomy existence; he hadn't realised how dark he'd let his world become until she'd shone her light upon him.

Without warning, he felt the walls of the bungalow close in around him, and he had to get out. Throwing the bedclothes aside and leaping to his feet, he hastily dressed, made his ablutions and was out of the door in ten minutes.

When he found himself on Nessa's doorstep it came as no surprise.

'Good morning,' she said, opening the door. A slow smile spread across her face, and he longed to kiss her. 'Off out to buy a paper?'

'No, I... er...'

'Come in. I've spoken to the hospital, but all they'd say is that Mairi's comfortable.'

'Shall we visit her again today?' he asked, following her into the kitchen.

'The ward sister said her daughter is back in the country and will be calling in later, so maybe not. Too many visitors might wear her out.'

'Oh, OK.' Now what should he say? 'Would you like to go out with me?' came out of his mouth before he had a chance to consider the words. Damn, he'd sounded like a fourteen-year-old.

'You mean like boyfriend and girlfriend? That sort of going out?' Nessa's expression was quizzical.

'Um, if you like, although I meant go out somewhere today.'

'Ah. I see.' Nessa's gaze dropped to the floor, and he worried that he'd embarrassed her.

'I'd like to be your boyfriend,' he said, then worried even more that he'd just sounded creepy.

Nessa looked up at him from underneath her lashes. 'That's settled, then. We're officially dating.'

'We *are*? Yes!' He reined himself in, not wanting to make a bigger fool of himself than he already had done.

She giggled, and her laugh was infectious and set him to chuckling.

'You'd have thought it would get easier as one gets older,' he said.

'I suppose it depends on how much practice you have. Personally, I've not had much these last twenty years.'

'Me, neither,' he admitted and they grinned at each other. He couldn't decide whether to kiss her whilst he thought about where he could take her. He supposed he'd better wine and dine her, but it was too early in the day for that. Besides, not only did he not want to wait until this evening, he didn't have a clue where to go. The Busy Bumble was the only place he could think of, but he didn't fancy it, even though it was the sole place he could take her to without asking her to drive. There were too many people who knew him, and he didn't think he could bear to be stared at and whispered about. And he had no doubt they would – he'd not stepped foot in the pub for years. And he'd never been seen in the company of a woman either. The villagers would have a field day gossiping about him.

He was spared having to say anything by a knock on the door.

Nessa raised her eyebrows. 'I wonder who that could be; I'm not expecting anyone.'

George prayed it was a delivery driver or some such, and not a member of Applewell's community. There'd be more than eyebrows raised if anyone saw him in Nessa's house.

'Hi, I'm Alison,' he heard a woman's voice say, when Nessa went to see who it was. 'I've just come from the hospital. Thank you so much for being there for my mum.'

'Do come in. How is she?' Nessa led a woman around his age into the kitchen, and George got to his feet. 'This is George – he lives in the bungalow next door. Would you like a cup of tea?'

'No, thanks, I can't stay.' Alison had dark smudges under her eyes and lines around her mouth. 'I only popped in for a second to see Mum, as it was so early. I went straight to the hospital from the airport, but I'll visit her properly this afternoon.' She sighed. 'Mum's as well as can be expected, whatever that means. I managed to catch the doctor on his ward rounds, but I couldn't get a lot out of him. They are assessing her and running tests, but they won't commit to anything, and they keep saying strokes affect people in different ways.'

'How is she in herself?' Nessa asked.

'Frightened, weak, a bit confused. I think this will be a long road. Anyway, I just wanted to pop by and say thank you. Also I need to ask you, how much do I owe you for sorting out my mum's door?'

George kept his head down and mumbled, 'Nothing.' He was pleased to have helped, but he wasn't comfortable having anyone make a fuss about it.

'You must have got someone in to board it up?' Alison insisted.

'Not really.' He winced, avoiding her gaze. He could hear the grumpiness in his voice, but he couldn't help it.

'George boarded Mairi's front door up himself,' Nessa intervened. 'He's clever like that.'

'Then I need to pay you for the materials,' Alison insisted.

He shook his head. 'No need.'

'He's got a shed full of offcuts of stuff – he used one of those,' Nessa explained, and he was glad she did because George wasn't comfortable blowing his own trumpet.

'A man came out to take a look at it,' he blurted. Mairi's daughter needed to know this bit. 'It needs a complete new door and frame. I went ahead and ordered it, the same as she's got now. Sorry. I'm happy to pay for it.' He cringed inside, hoping he'd done the right thing, and convinced he hadn't.

'Don't be silly!' Alison cried. 'If you give me the details, I'll take it from here. I'll have to speak to them today anyway and see how soon they can fix it, because I was hoping to stay there while mum is in hospital.'

'I've got a key to the back door,' he said. 'I'll go and fetch it.'

'Would you? That's so kind.'

George was glad to escape back to his house for a few minutes. Having Nessa speak up for him was cringe-worthy; although he had appreciated it, he'd found his embarrassment difficult to deal with. He'd always found receiving praise hard, and he found being thanked even harder to accept.

He'd put Mairi's backdoor key on his desk where he knew it wouldn't get lost, so he grabbed it and returned to Nessa's house, hoping the two women wouldn't be chatting for long.

'Here you go,' he said, handing Alison the key.

'Thank you so much for everything you've done,' she gushed, and George shrank into himself.

'You're welcome,' he muttered, staring hard at the floor.

'Give our love to Mairi when you see her this afternoon, and tell her we'll visit her tomorrow, if that's OK?'

'I'm sure it will be. I'll go back to Swansea after I've seen her today, and then drive back up tomorrow, so I'll visit in the evening. I dropped my husband at our house, along with our cases, so I need to go home and pick him up. We'll stay in Mum's house for a few days until we know what's what.'

'I'm sure she'll be fine,' Nessa said, but George could tell she was still worried about Mairi. 'If there's anything we can do, just shout,' she added.

'That's very kind of you.' Alison fingered the key. 'Right, I suppose I'd better pack her some more things. I think she'll be in hospital a while.'

Nessa showed her out, and George listened with half an ear to the conversation. The other half was listening to Sylvia's pneumatic purring as she rubbed her face against his leg.

He bent to stroke her head, marvelling at how silky it was. He hadn't had a great deal to do with animals, although he'd watched a fair amount of nature documentaries in his time. Cats were an enigma to him, although he was able to recognise the breed.

Sylvia stood on her hind paws and pushed her face into his hand.

'She likes you,' Nessa said, making him jump. He hadn't heard her come back into the living room and he was mildly embarrassed to be caught petting her cat.

Embarrassed appeared to be his middle name this morning, and he told himself to get over it. It was perfectly normal to stroke a cat – that's why people owned such creatures. And now that he'd tried it, he could see the attraction. She was rather sweet and quite loving, which was a surprise because he'd always been led to believe that cats were solitary and distant. Just like him.

'I like her,' he admitted. 'She's very friendly.' He hesitated. 'Can I ask you something? Why did you have her on a leash the day you moved in? I didn't think you could take cats for a walk.'

'Some people walk their cats regularly, but Sylvia was only on a lead because I didn't want her to wander off and get lost.'

'I see.'

'You thought I was a crazy woman, didn't you?'

'Might have…'

'Are you sure you want to date a crazy woman?'

He could tell she was teasing. 'I'm sure.'

'In that case, you asked if I wanted to go out somewhere. How do you feel about a visit to a garden centre? I know it's not very romantic, but that's what I was planning to do today. My garden is a mess – I need to buy a new lawnmower for a start, and I'd like to have some pretty flower beds and maybe a water feature in the garden.'

'I can mend the lawnmower,' George offered. 'If you like.'

'You can?'

He nodded. He could maybe even make a water feature, if she wanted. He was certain there was an old barrel in his shed which would do. He didn't think he had a pump though. Water features weren't something his father had been into.

'That would be fantastic. But I'd still like to go to the garden centre.'

'So would I.' Not only had George never been to one and was curious, but he was happy to go anywhere Nessa wanted, if it meant being with her.

The way he was feeling, he never wanted to let her out of his sight.

Chapter 38

Nessa

There was something very civilised and middle-class about wandering around a garden centre, Nessa thought. It was also nice to have George with her, and she felt like they were a proper couple. Noticing their reflection in the glass as they approached the sliding doors, Nessa decided they looked right together, and she had a weird feeling that this was meant to be, that they were destined to be together.

She knew it was daft, this idea of there being The One, of everyone having a soul-mate, but deep down she was quietly hopeful she'd found hers. After all these years of being alone, she'd found someone she thought she would be happy to spend her life with.

What absurd thoughts to be having on a Wednesday afternoon in the middle of Nature's Garden Centre, she thought, laughing inwardly at herself. She hardly knew George, yet here she was planning on spending the rest of her life with him.

But the thought refused to budge, and just how much more did she need to know anyway? She knew George was kind and thoughtful beneath his gruff and antisocial demeanour. She knew he was damaged and lonely, and stuck in a rut. She knew he felt something for her, but how deeply she wasn't sure. But most of all, she knew she was falling in love with him, slowly and surely.

There were so many facets to him, and this afternoon she was treated to his playful side.

'George, where are you?' she called.

They'd been exploring the summer house and shed area of the garden centre, and she'd been seriously considering the idea of putting one at the top of the garden, where it would receive the most sun. She could imagine herself enjoying a glass of wine on a chilly autumn evening, with George and a fire pit beside her to keep her warm. But she was just about to suggest it, when she noticed he'd disappeared.

'George?' He couldn't have gone far. He'd been right behind her, running his hands over the planed wood of a veranda attached to a rather nice garden room.

She saw that the door to a garden room was slightly ajar and she wondered if he might have gone inside. There was no sign of him through the window, but she pushed the door open anyway and—

'Eek!' He'd stepped out from behind the door, grabbed her around the waist and swung her into him. She came up hard against his chest and felt the raw strength in his forearms as he held her tight.

'Do you mind?' he asked gruffly, and his head dipped towards hers.

For a moment she was worried someone might see, but then she realised she didn't care. Kissing him was what she wanted to do, and it didn't matter if a couple of middle-aged ladies saw them snogging. The surging feeling inside was so strong, she couldn't begin to deny it.

She moulded herself to him, tipped her head up and closed her eyes. His lips were a mere flutter at first, and her stomach was full of dancing butterflies, her knees trembled and she found it hard to breathe.

When he deepened the kiss, she thought she might faint. The blood was singing in her veins, she could feel a pulse in her throat, and her heart was pounding so hard she thought it might jump out of her chest. Dear God, what was this man doing to her?

Desire coursed through her, and she pulled away with a gasp.

He was immediately contrite. 'I'm sorry—' he started, but she put a finger to his lips.

'Don't be, I like kissing you; I like kissing you very much indeed, but not here. I'm scared I might do something I regret.'

'Oh?' His eyebrows arched and she felt his lips move under her finger as he began to smile. Hastily she dropped her hand to her side – she'd been very tempted to slip her finger into his mouth and—

Oh no, she wasn't going there, not right now and not right *here*, although she would dearly love to take it further, and she could tell he did, too. His eyes were bright, his lips slightly parted, and he seemed to be having as much difficulty as she was in catching his breath. She dared not glance at him again for fear of what she might see, so she reached for his hand, gave it a squeeze, then slipped out of the door, leaving him to compose himself.

When he came out after a minute or so, she calmly suggested they visit the garden centre's cafe and have some lunch.

'Nothing heavy,' she said, 'just a sandwich or a salad, enough to tide us over until this evening.'

He opened his mouth to speak, cleared his throat and coughed, before starting again. 'Good idea, I am rather hungry.' Then he smiled, and looked away, leaving her under no illusion what it was he hungered for.

Liquid heat swept through her, and she bit her lip, resisting the urge to drag him back into the garden room and finish what they'd started.

It was quite heady this feeling of not being in control of herself, of feeling wanton and a little bit naughty. She couldn't remember the last time she had such a reaction to a man. She wanted George and he very clearly wanted her.

A thought struck her with such force that her knees felt weak. What was stopping them? Nessa couldn't think of a single thing. They were both adults, they were both single, and they had no one else to answer to.

'Stuff it!' she exclaimed. 'I don't want to bother with lunch. Do you?'

The look he gave her turned her legs to jelly. 'No, I don't.' His voice was low and throaty, and throwing caution to the wind, she grabbed his hand, and dragged him through the garden centre and out into the car park.

All thoughts of buying plants or water features were forgotten. The only thing she could think about was getting home and taking him upstairs.

George didn't appear to have anything to say, either; he just kept sending her heated glances which warmed her cheek and seared her heart.

But once she pulled the car up onto the drive, and they got out and went into her house, the pair of them seemed to be struck by an attack of the collywobbles. They came to a halt in the hall, and neither of them could look the other in the eye.

Crikey, this was awkward, she thought, and swiftly resorted to what any middle-aged British woman would do under the circumstances.

'I'll put the kettle on, shall I?' she said, and slipped past him into the kitchen. She could feel him following behind her, but he didn't close the gap between them. Instead, he propped himself up against the door frame and watched as she busied herself making them a cup of tea.

'Are you hungry?' she asked, risking a quick look at him and then wishing she hadn't as she saw a flare of desire in his eyes.

'Yes.'

'Shall I make us something?'

'If you want.'

'I could do us a sandwich.'

She heard him mutter an oath under his breath, then he covered the distance between them in two short strides. This was more like it, she thought, as he swept her into his arms, and held her fast.

'Do you really want a sandwich?' he asked, and Nessa let out a nervous giggle.

'Not really.'

'I didn't think so,' he growled, and he went to kiss her, but she leant away from him. The momentary hurt which flashed in his eyes soon fled, to be replaced by dawning understanding when she took both his hands in hers and backed slowly out of the room, only stopping when they arrived at the bottom of the stairs and she was forced to let go of one of his hands. The other she grasped firmly, as she tugged him up the first step.

'Are you sure about this?' he asked.

'I've never been surer about anything in my life,' she said, and then she proceeded to show him exactly how sure she was.

Chapter 39

Nessa

Nessa hadn't thought she'd ever glowed before, but this morning when she looked in the mirror it was amazing just how glowy she was. Her eyes sparkled, there was a dewy softness to her skin, and her lips looked plumper than they had ever done before – although, that might be because they were slightly bruised from all that kissing, and other stuff.

Remembering the other stuff brought a deeper glow to her cheeks.

My God, she didn't know he had it in him. She certainly wouldn't have thought it to look at him. He was a dark horse, indeed.

They'd spent the rest of the afternoon yesterday in bed, only driven from it by hunger. But even making themselves some supper hadn't been without incident, and she made a note to give the kitchen table a good scrub.

Then they'd gone back to bed, and had stayed there until this morning, when Sylvia's disgruntled wailing had forced her to get up and see to the poor moggie. Sylvia clearly hadn't approved of the bedroom door being firmly shut, with her mistress on one side of it and her on the other. Nessa might have been tempted to let the cat in, and she would have done so if there had been anything in the way of sleep going on. But they hadn't slept much at all, so Sylvia had remained firmly outside.

Aware that she should be exhausted this morning, but feeling the total opposite, Nessa had taken a shower (so had George – at the same time) and then she'd made them some breakfast.

Chocolate pancakes with blueberries and strawberries had gone down a treat, and she had thoroughly enjoyed letting George feed her from his own plate. The act was almost as intimate as what they'd done last night and this morning. And what she hoped they would do again later on today.

For now though, she was on her own in the cottage, George having gone back to his bungalow. Regretfully he'd told her he had to do some work, having not done any for a few days. She could tell he didn't want to leave, but he did so anyway, with the promise of seeing her again later this afternoon so they could visit Mairi together.

Too exuberant to stay indoors, Nessa decided to go for a walk. She was running low on eggs and milk, so a stroll into Applewell wouldn't go amiss.

It was another brilliantly sunny day, the weather reflecting Nessa's mood. She felt bouncy and happy, unable to sit still for a second, and she almost skipped into the village, conscious she was wearing an idiotic smile on her face, but unable to do anything about it. She couldn't be serious if she tried today. Joy was bubbling out of her and she felt like singing and dancing, but she settled for humming quietly to herself as she walked along the main street.

When she passed by the cafe, a sudden rapping on the glass made her jump, and she let out a squeak.

Eleri was peering through the window, and when Nessa turned to look at her, she beckoned her inside. Nessa gave a mental shrug and decided she might as well. Maybe a slice of cake and a cup of coffee would calm her down.

'I haven't seen you in ages,' Eleri said. 'How are you keeping?'

'I'm good, thanks,' Nessa replied, trying to keep her smile within socially acceptable limits.

'I heard about Mairi. How is she?'

'They're still running tests, I think. Her daughter came by yesterday, but she didn't have much more news. We're going to visit her this afternoon, so we might know a bit more.'

'Sit down, I'll fetch you a slice of cake and a tea on the house for what you did for Mairi.'

'Oh, it was nothing,' Nessa said, sadly. 'I just wish we'd gotten to her sooner.'

'If it wasn't for you, it might have been too late.'

'I suppose.'

'When you say *we*, you mean you and George, don't you? I hear you two have been getting quite cosy.'

'He's just a friend,' Nessa hastened to tell her, crossing her fingers under the table to ward off the evil for telling a lie. She didn't want to deny their relationship, but she wasn't sure whether George would want it broadcast around the village. She wasn't sure she did, either. The whole thing was so new, so precious, that she wanted to keep it to herself for a while.

'You were seen, you know. Kissing on the beach.'

Nessa pressed her lips together.

'Don't worry, everyone is really happy for you both, and especially for George. It's about time he came out of his shell a bit. We've all been getting quite worried about him.' She paused and narrowed her eyes. Nessa tried to keep her expression blank, but she didn't think it worked. Especially when Eleri said, 'Have you been out in the sun? You've got a glow about you.' Then she chortled, leaving Nessa under no illusion what she was referring to.

Thankfully, Eleri moved away to fetch her order, leaving Nessa slightly shell-shocked. You couldn't keep a secret in a place like Applewell, could you, she said to herself. When George found out, he'd be mortified. He was such a private and insular man, that she didn't know how he'd react knowing everyone was aware of their relationship. And what they didn't know, as Eleri had once told her, they would probably make up. But in this instance, they would be right.

But it didn't matter what anyone else thought, did it? The only people who mattered were her and George. And as long as they were happy with the way things were going between them, no one else's opinion should matter. Although Nessa was secretly pleased that Eleri was happy for them.

Talking about being happy, Nessa couldn't remember ever being as happy as she was now. All she hoped was that George felt the same way. He filled her mind and her heart, and although she acknowledged they still had some way to go, she felt extremely positive about their relationship, about him and about life in general.

The only blot on her perfect landscape was Mairi.

—

Nessa didn't tell George about her visit to the cafe, and neither did she share Eleri's comments with him; she didn't think he was ready, and she was certain it might upset him.

Anyway, he didn't give her a chance to say anything when he arrived on her doorstep at the designated time. Instead, he picked her up and swung her around, kissing her until she was giddy.

'You're going to have to stop doing that,' she said, gasping for breath and laughing. 'I'm not going to be able to drive.'

'That's something else I need to think about,' George said to her. 'I've decided I'm going to try to see if my car works. It seems a shame to have it sitting in the garage doing nothing for all these years, when I could have been driving it.' He gave her a sheepish look. 'Although, saying that, I didn't have anywhere to drive to, or anyone to go with. But it's not fair you doing all the driving, so I need to get my backside into gear, get the car working again and sort out the necessary paperwork. Then I can do my share of the driving while you sit in the passenger seat and stare at *me* longingly.'

'Is that what you do?' she asked.

'I can't help it – you're gorgeous.'

She gave him a brilliant smile as they got in the car and drove off. 'You can stare at me as much as you like,' she added. 'I don't mind.'

'I want to do more than just stare,' was his answering growl, and Nessa shivered with delight.

It seemed disrespectful to be so happy when poor Mairi was unwell in hospital, so Nessa tried to tamp down her emotions and put a serious look on her face as they walked onto Mairi's ward.

'How are you, my lovely?' Nessa asked bending over the old lady and kissing her cheek.

Mairi looked brighter, but she still seemed incredibly frail. 'When can I go home?' she asked, and Nessa sent George a charged look, willing him not to say anything.

She had been asked this question many times in the past, and she had always been noncommittal unless she had firm information from whichever doctor was overseeing the patient's case.

'You can come home when the doctor says you can,' Nessa told her in her best nurse's voice. 'You have to listen to the experts; they know what they're doing.'

'I want to go home,' was Mairi's firm response. She reached out a hand across the bedclothes, and Nessa grasped it. Her friend had surprising strength, Nessa was pleased to note, as her hand was squeezed.

'Alison says I might have to go and live with her,' Mairi said. 'I don't want to.'

'You mightn't want to, but sometimes what we want isn't necessarily what's best for us.'

Mairi stared from Nessa to George and back again. 'What you want is certainly doing you some good, my girl,' she said. She turned to George. 'It looks like you took my advice and—'

George leapt in with, 'We're getting your front door fixed,' and Nessa tried not to smile, guessing that whatever advice Mairi had given him the other day wasn't something George wanted to share with her.

They stayed with Mairi for a good hour or so, until Nessa could see she was starting to get tired. They promised to visit her again shortly, and as they were walking out of the hospital Nessa suggested that they take a stroll around Aberystwyth.

'It seems a shame to have driven all this way, and not make full use of the rest of the afternoon,' she said.

George gave her a look that made her tingle right down to her toes.

'I'm not saying that spending the rest of the day in bed would be a waste,' she clarified, 'but I haven't seen anything of the town yet apart from the hospital and I wouldn't mind stretching my legs and having a bit of fresh air. We'll work up an appetite.'

George gave her another of those looks, and she rolled her eyes. 'You're naughty,' she told him.

'Sorry,' he said cheerfully, clearly not meaning it, and she slapped him playfully on the arm.

'Come on you, I fancy hot fish and chips with lots of salt and vinegar. I bet you haven't had lunch, have you?'

He shook his head.

'That's decided then,' she said, and she made him guide her into the centre of Aberystwyth where they parked the car near the marina.

'Shall we take a stroll along the promenade?' he suggested. 'We can walk as far as the pier and there's bound to be a fish and chip shop nearby. We can sit on a bench on the seafront to eat them and then, if you like, we can have an ice cream and walk up to the castle. It's not too far and it's not too high, but the view out over Cardigan Bay is stunning. What do you say?'

Nessa thought it sounded perfect, so that's what they did.

There was something particularly wonderful about strolling hand in hand along the seafront on a gorgeous sunny day, she thought as she took a deep breath, filling her lungs with fresh sea air, and she smiled happily. Glancing at George out of the corner of her eye, she saw that he looked happy, too, and her heart was suddenly filled with love for him.

She wasn't *falling* for him. She had *fallen* – head over heels – and she was amazed it had happened so fast and so unexpectedly.

It was very early into their relationship to have such intense feelings, and the strength of them astounded her. It also took some of the shine off the day as she agonised over whether there was any possibility he felt the same way.

Nessa could tell he cared for her, but love was a different prospect entirely.

There was no way she was going to let him know just yet how deep her emotions ran. She was terrified of making a fool of herself, and not only that, she worried she might scare him off, and she didn't want to do anything which might jeopardise their relationship.

Time would give her the answer to her question. If he began to feel for her what she felt for him, then it would show eventually.

This insight about her new feelings came as a surprise, however. She hadn't been looking for love, and she certainly hadn't expected to find it in her grumpy next-door neighbour. But find it she had, and now she intended to nurture it. Aside from the usual flutters she felt whenever George was near (or whenever she thought about him, for that matter), she now felt the weight of this new revelation resting heavily in her heart.

She was still mulling it over as they ate their fish and chips, sitting on a bench looking out to sea. It was in the forefront of her mind as they each chose an ice-cream flavour, then wandered up to the castle taking turns to share each other's ice cream, the flavours mixing on their tongues. On the drive back it was still there, hovering at the edge of her thoughts, and she didn't know whether to be excited by it or terrified.

If she was honest, terror was gaining the upper hand. Mainly because this was very new to her and, despite having been married in the past, she was now older and more set in her ways, and she hadn't been looking for love. Although, to be honest, neither had she been discounting it. But the fact that it had happened so quickly after moving to Applewell had knocked her for six, and she was dwelling on it so much that George asked if she was all right.

'Don't mind me,' she said, 'I'm fine. I'm just a little worried about Mairi.' It was the truth, sort of. But now she had something else to worry about.

Deciding she couldn't do anything about her feelings, and acknowledging she wasn't going to share them with George, Nessa made a very conscious effort to push the 'L' word to the back of her mind.

When they got back to her house, Nessa made them both a cup of tea, and they sat on the sofa in her living room to drink it, George cuddling up to her.

'We're going to have to pay the garden centre another visit,' Nessa said, giggling as she remembered how she'd come away empty-handed. 'And this time you're going to have to stop me from dragging you out from there and taking you to bed.'

'You're seriously telling me that I'm going to have to stop you from taking me to bed?' he asked, stroking the back of her head and twisting his fingers through her hair. 'I don't think I can. Resisting you isn't easy.'

'So what you're saying is that all I have to do is click my fingers and you'll be up those stairs quicker than Sylvia chasing a mouse?'

'That's exactly what I'm saying.'

Nessa put her mug on the coffee table and swivelled around to face him. She snapped her fingers.

George grinned at her. He stood up and walked towards the door. 'Well, are you coming?'

Nessa had always been a fan of the double entendre. 'Ooh, yes please!'

Chapter 40

George

George was eating breakfast, although it was proving difficult to butter toast one-handed, as the other one was clasped firmly around Nessa's smaller more delicate one. They were holding hands across Nessa's kitchen table and beaming at each other like lovesick teenagers.

George was loving every second of it. Nessa appeared to be content with the situation, too, but he'd have to let go of her hand soon, otherwise he'd be forced to eat his toast dry.

'Have you got anything planned for today?' Nessa asked, and George felt his face fall.

'Unfortunately, I do have some work to do. I've promised to have these accounts back to their owner by Monday. If I have a good go at them today, I might very well get them done. How about you?'

'I'll probably potter around here for a while, maybe pop into the village and pick up some supplies for our tea.'

George winced. It wasn't fair that she cooked all the time, in the same way it wasn't fair that she drove all the time. He could probably do something about the driving; the cooking was a slightly different matter due to his kitchen being unusable for the most part.

He should take her out to dinner, but once again he was reluctant for all the reasons he'd thought about before. If he didn't want Nessa to drive, then it would have to be the Busy Bumble. He hadn't stepped foot in the pub for years, and he wasn't sure he was looking forward to stepping foot in it now, but Nessa deserved it. He was aware of his limitations, and he was very aware of some of his other personality traits. What he didn't want, was for them to restrict what he and Nessa did. He'd been restricted and confined by his own insecurities and fears for so long, he knew it was going to be difficult to release himself from their shackles, but if that was what he had to do to be one half of a normal couple, then that's what he would do.

He was also fully aware that there was no such thing as 'normal'. But he wanted Nessa to enjoy the things he knew other couples did – going to the cinema, going out for meals, having friends around for dinner. Hold the last one; he wasn't quite ready for that, although he could quite easily imagine him, Nessa and Mairi sitting around a table having Sunday lunch.

What he really dreaded, he realised, was not so much going out for a meal itself, after all eating fish and chips out yesterday had been perfectly fine, and the day before he would have been more than happy to have had lunch at the garden centre. It was the stares, the nudges and the comments of the residents of Applewell that he feared.

He'd been secretive and reclusive for such a long time, that having anyone else know his business was anathema to him. Yet a little voice in his head was telling him he'd allowed Nessa in, and to a certain extent Mairi, too, so it shouldn't be too difficult to let the villagers see that he and Nessa were an item.

He could cope with that, just. What he couldn't cope with was anyone other than Nessa knowing what lay behind the front door of his bungalow.

'Earth to George,' Nessa teased, squeezing his hand.

He gave her a squeeze back, then released her and buttered his now-cold toast. 'Do you fancy going to the Busy Bumble for supper?' he asked, before she could enquire what he'd been thinking about.

Nessa's eyes widened. 'Are you sure?'

'Yes.'

'Then I'd love to.'

'It's a date,' he said, and he smiled at her giggle. He loved hearing that sound, and he loved even more that he was the one that was responsible for it.

Toast eaten, he left Nessa with a loudly demanding Silvia, and went back to the bungalow to do a spot of work.

He hadn't spent an awful lot of time in his own home recently, and every time he returned to it he became more and more conscious of the state it was in. He couldn't help comparing it to the clutter-free spaciousness of Nessa's little cottage, and neither could he help feeling that the longer he stayed away, the less the bungalow felt like home.

He was grateful for a chance to be alone for a moment, though – not that he didn't want to be with Nessa (he wanted that more than anything he'd ever wanted in his life), but he welcomed the opportunity to mull over the events of the last few days.

Magical, heart-stopping, tear-inducing were just a few of the words that sprang to mind, together with some earthier ones. He was smitten, totally and utterly captivated by her to the extent that he didn't want to share her, even with the clientele of the Busy Bumble this evening.

He froze as an unwelcome thought occurred to him – was he in danger of hoarding Nessa's time, and possibly her affection, in the same way he hoarded other things? Maybe... Or perhaps he was so in love with her he couldn't bear to share her. Not yet, not when everything was so new.

But share her he must. Nessa had so much love to give, so much kindness to share, he couldn't possibly try to keep it all for himself. And he was proud of her, too, for having such a huge heart.

Giving himself a mental shake, George started up his computer and began doing what he was paid to do, losing himself in the purity of numbers for several hours until the accounts were finally done.

He got to his feet and stretched, being very careful not to move too much in any particular direction. The last thing he needed right now was to knock anything over – the resulting domino effect didn't bear thinking about. He'd go back to Nessa's house (the bedroom came to mind), and spend the rest of the afternoon with her before they went out later, and he was about to leave, when he stopped and looked around what had once been his living room. *Really* looked at it.

George almost didn't recognise it. He certainly didn't recognise the patches of patterned wallpaper just visible in places. It was very 1980s and was in dire need of stripping off and redoing. Although he was no expert on interior design, even he knew it was out-dated and old-fashioned. Just like him in a way, and he couldn't expect Nessa to spend any time here even if the bungalow was eventually cleared.

Heck, *he* didn't want to spend any time here either, but that was likely because of the memories contained in these walls and not solely down to the décor.

When he compared Nessa's home to his own, he knew which he preferred.

Suddenly, he couldn't wait to clear the place. The sooner the bungalow was free of all the things he and his father had hung onto over the years, the sooner he himself would be free. Perhaps not totally free, but *freer*. And, in the back of his mind, was the hope that if he made the bungalow attractive enough, one day he'd be able to ask Nessa to share it with him.

He found Nessa in the garden where she was sitting on the overgrown patio and reading a book.

'Will you help me sort out a few things?' he blurted. He'd never have the courage or the strength to do this alone.

'Of course,' Nessa said, putting her book down. 'When would you like to start?'

George swallowed. 'Um…?'

'Tomorrow? Maybe we could start with the hall?' she suggested.

It was the logical place, then they could work their way into the kitchen.

Or, maybe not. Abruptly, he felt cold. This was going too fast for his liking. If he wasn't careful, he'd be knee-deep in plastic bags and Nessa would be sporting a pair of Marigolds and wielding a duster.

'OK. Have you any ideas what you'd like to do with all those newspapers?' Nessa continued and George's heart turned over.

'No…' Oh God, this was hard. At least she hadn't suggested hiring a skip, or at the very least, filling up the pristine and unused paper recycling bin the council had provided. Yet.

He wracked his brains. 'Um, they can be used for cleaning windows.' He remembered his mother doing that when he was small, when the windows in the bungalow could still be reached from the inside. He'd also been known to clean the outside on occasion with a tabloid or two since then.

He liked that she was leaving the decisions to him. Perversely, he also wished she'd make them for him, but she was probably astute enough to realise that if she did, he'd pooh-pooh the suggestion. This had to come from him. But although he'd told her he was ready, he wondered if he truly was.

'Anything else?' she asked. 'I can't see you going around people's houses and asking if they'd like a copy of *The Daily Trumpet* to clean their windows with.'

George's mind went blank and it must have shown on his face.

'Why don't we look up some ideas of what you can do with old newspapers?' Nessa suggested.

'OK...'

Nessa reached for her mobile and jabbed at it. Then she handed it to him. 'Take a look.'

George hesitantly looked at the results, and one by one, he read them out. The last suggestion was to put them in the recycling bin, which he wasn't at all happy with.

Nessa said, 'I like the idea of using them for gift-wrapping, or making fire-bricks out of them. Moulding them into biodegradable pots for seedlings is a fab idea too. I've never had a go at papier mâché, though, have you?'

'Would you like to try?'

'It might be fun. What would we make?'

'We'll think about it later,' he promised, because suddenly his mind wasn't on newspapers or their assorted uses – he was focusing on the light in her eyes, and her upturned lips as she smiled, and another activity popped into his head. 'Right now, I think there's something else we could make…?'

To George's delight, it seemed that Nessa didn't need asking twice.

Chapter 41

Nessa

The Busy Bumble was living up to its name, Nessa saw, when she and George walked into the pub later. It wasn't quite packed, but most of the tables were taken and several men were clustered around the bar, pints in their hands. She recognised Tony from Pins to Elephants, and one or two others who she didn't yet know by name.

George headed for a free table in the corner, and she noticed his gaze was locked firmly on his target. He didn't catch anyone's eye and neither did he acknowledge anyone's presence.

From the set of his shoulders and the stiffness of his back as she followed him, she knew this was a mistake. He might have sat on the seafront and eaten fish and chips with her, he might have been happy enough to have had lunch in the garden centre, but he'd been anonymous in both of those places. No one had known him, no one had given him a second glance.

But here, in this pub in the heart of the village he'd grown up in, the village he'd been forced to return to, he was in the spotlight. And Nessa realised that the noise in the bar had dimmed when they'd opened the door. It was enough to be noticeable.

Not everyone turned to look at George, but Nessa suspected that was because not everyone was a local. The people at most of the tables were tourists and hadn't taken the slightest bit of notice. But enough of the rest of the clientele had stopped to look to make her feel awkward.

As she took a seat opposite George, who had his back to the room, she was aware of the nudges and the mouths moving behind cupped hands.

She was also aware of the kind looks and the wide smiles sent in their direction, and she understood that what Eleri had said was right – people were pleased to see George out for once, and even more pleased to see he had a companion.

Nessa was about to mention it, when she caught sight of George's closed expression, and her heart went out to him. It must be so hard for him, but it would get easier, she knew. It was just that the villagers were unused to him doing anything other than taking his twice-daily walks to the shop – this was a novelty for them. Once they became accustomed to seeing him around a bit more, and in places he didn't usually frequent, she guessed their interest in him would wane. After all, she and George were hardly anything to write home about. They were two ordinary people, leading ordinary lives.

'Awright?' one of the men standing at the bar, called. 'Nice evening for it.'

Nessa nodded and smiled, then hissed out of the corner of her mouth, 'What's it a nice evening for, do you know?'

George's lips twisted and his face bore a pained expression. 'That's Donald Mousel,' he whispered back. 'He always says that. I'm never sure what he means, either.'

'OK...' She turned her attention back to Donald. 'It is, isn't it?' she said brightly.

'Shh, don't encourage him.' George looked panicked. 'I don't want to talk to him. I don't want to talk to anyone.'

'You don't have to, if you don't want to,' she assured him. 'Would you like to leave? I can always rustle something up.'

She saw him take a deep breath and straighten his shoulders. 'No, we're here now.'

Good, she thought, guessing that getting up and leaving now would cause more interest than by simply staying where they were and eating their food. They didn't have to linger; as soon as they'd finished eating they could go.

Nessa reached underneath the table, found his knee and patted it. His hands were clasped in his lap, but at her touch, he placed one of them over hers and held it tightly.

Bless him, he was so nervous and uncomfortable. If she had realised he'd react like this, she would have turned down his offer.

Yet, on the other hand, she understood if he was able to get through this, then it wouldn't be as bad next time. And she really did hope there'd be a next time. She had visions of dinner at the Busy Bumble being a regular Friday night thing, filled with love, laughter and good food. Maybe even joining another couple for a meal, or taking part in the pub quiz night she'd seen advertised the last time she'd been here. Nessa had a feeling George might be very good at answering quiz questions.

Nessa recognised George had some way to go before he got to such a stage of easy familiarity with the other villagers, but she had no doubt he would get there eventually. She'd see to that. It might take him a while to understand that everyone wished him the best and they were happy for him, but once he'd got his head around the fact that they weren't judging him, and they weren't being nosey (OK, they were – just a bit – but for all the right reasons), then he'd relax and begin to enjoy himself.

She'd seen the way he could be when he let his guard down, and it was wonderful. All she hoped was he might be able to do the same around the village. He was funny, in his own way, kind, loving, passionate (she blushed when she recalled just how passionate he could be), thoughtful—

'What can I get you?' a woman's voice asked, and Nessa recognised her as the waitress who'd served her and Mairi Sunday lunch. Crikey, was that only last Sunday? It seemed ages ago, so much had happened since.

They gave their drinks orders – George staring resolutely at the table – and Nessa asked for a couple of menus. The pair of them then sat in silence until the woman returned with a couple of glasses and a menu each.

Thankfully, the noise level in the room had returned to normal and Nessa noticed fewer looks as people went back to their own conversations.

'I fancy the Cumberland sausage and mash,' she said, closing her menu and putting it on the table.

'I'll have the same,' George said, but she didn't think he was in the least bit interested in what he ate.

Nessa called the waitress over, handed the menus back and told her what they both wanted, then she settled back in her chair and tried to put George more at ease. It was easier said than done, because to her he looked as though he was wound up tighter than a spring and was ready to bounce out of his seat and make a dash for the door.

He didn't though, and she had to admire him for that. He was clearly not enjoying the experience one bit, but he was sticking with it, and she was proud of him.

Over George's shoulder, she saw Tony put his pint down on the bar, thump the man called Donald on his shoulder, and look their way. She assumed Tony was leaving, but instead he started to walk over to their table.

Nessa stiffened and said, without moving her lips, 'Don't look now, but the man who owns Pins to Elephants is on his way over.'

George froze and to Nessa he looked as though he was about to bolt. She smiled at him reassuringly, and his grip tightened on her hand.

'George, Nessa.' Tony nodded to them both.

Nessa said, 'Hi.' George said nothing.

'Nice to see you out and about of an evening,' Tony said, directing the comment to George, who remained silent. 'I just wanted to say thanks. It's good to know Mairi has neighbours like you. I dread to think what would have happened if you two hadn't been there.'

Nessa said, 'I thank God we were there, too.'

George still said nothing.

'And you boarded up her front door. John Porter was telling me you made a decent job of it, too. He said he would have done it had he known, but I said you've probably got enough bits of board in your shed to cover the whole house. It's lucky you don't get rid of anything, because you never know when summat will come in handy. Mind you, I suppose it'll take years to find a use for all the stuff you've been hoarding.' He chuckled and clapped George on the shoulder. 'Right, best be off. The missus will have my tea on the table, and she'll chew my ear off if I'm late.'

Nessa sat in stunned silence. She'd been watching George while Tony was speaking, and she'd seen his expression change from wary to shocked, to downright angry. He was furious, and she couldn't believe Tony had been so insensitive as to bring up the subject of George's hoarding. No wonder poor George didn't want to have anything to do with any of the villagers if they acted like this.

She knew Tony hadn't meant anything by it, and she guessed he probably didn't think he was saying anything out of turn. He probably didn't even realise that George was so sensitive about it.

But the damage had been done, and Nessa had a feeling George wouldn't want to have a meal in the Busy Bumble anytime soon. He probably wouldn't pay a visit to Pins to Elephants for a while, either. And he'd been making such good progress, too. She just hoped—

'I trusted you.' George's voice was so low Nessa had to strain to hear it above the noise in the bar. And when she did hear what he'd said, she thought she'd heard incorrectly.

'Pardon?'

'I can't believe you'd do that to me. I thought we had something.' His face was hard and she could see he was shaking.

What did he mean—? Oh, *oh, no*! 'I didn't—' she began, but he cut her off.

'I thought we were… you were… that I lo—' Abruptly, he stopped and leapt to his feet, knocking his chair over.

He didn't give her a chance to say anything further, but was striding to the door before Nessa was able to process what was happening.

Silence descended on the room, and she could feel the weight of everyone's stares.

Someone came over to her table and righted the upturned chair with a sympathetic smile.

Tony, who hadn't left yet, but had been working his way towards the door, chatting to people as he went, had a horrified look on his face. Nessa hoped it was because he'd realised what he'd said and the damage his careless words had done.

She didn't know how long she sat there, but it couldn't have been longer than a few minutes. Dimly she noticed their waitress approach her table carrying a basket of condiments and some cutlery, but someone intercepted her, and the woman turned smartly on her heel, and left Nessa alone.

After a while, people stopped looking at her, apart from the occasional glance, and they carried on their conversations.

But she was conscious of their curiosity and of their pity.

Slowly, feeling like an old woman, she got to her feet and made her way towards the door, her mind sluggish, her heart bleeding.

She didn't remember any of the walk home.

The only thing she remembered was reaching her drive and automatically looking at the bungalow.

There wasn't any sign of life.

There rarely ever was.

And she wondered what had made her believe there ever had been. Because without love there *was* no life – none that was worth living.

Chapter 42

George

It wasn't the greatest idea George had ever had, but digging his car out of the garage was the only thing he could focus on right now. There was a tonne of stuff to shift before he could clear the space between the vehicle and the garage doors, and trying to be as quiet as a mouse whilst he was doing it wasn't easy. If he was honest, he hadn't thought it through – all he knew was that he wanted to escape. Whether it was from the bungalow, Applewell or himself, was irrelevant. He had to go now, and he couldn't see any other way.

He stopped to wipe the sweat from his brow, but the second he paused in his frantic lifting and carrying, Nessa's shocked and horrified face flashed across his mind.

Refusing to think about her, he resolutely continued to stealthily move boxes, old doors, panes of glass, broken tools… wincing each time he made a noise, hoping Nessa hadn't heard.

He didn't want to see her or speak to her. Not now. Possibly not ever again. And if he could free his car, then he might never have to.

To his relief, she hadn't followed him out of the pub. He didn't know whether she was still there or whether she'd returned to her cottage, because he'd gone straight to the garage, squeezed and wriggled his way in through the side door, then had proceeded to empty it, not caring about the state of his garden as he stacked everything outside. The only person who'd see was Nessa if she looked out of her window. And if anyone else saw the mess, which was unlikely, what did it matter? Applewell knew all about his secret, so there was no point in hiding it any more.

He felt like crying, but he refused to give in. Tears wouldn't undo what he felt about her – despite what she'd done. And neither would they right the wrong she'd done him. He'd believed her when she'd told him that she wouldn't tell anyone about his hoarding.

But she had.

The sense of betrayal he felt was enormous.

His sense of loss was even bigger.

For the first time in what seemed forever, George wanted a shoulder to cry on. He wanted someone who'd tell him everything was going to be all right, even if it was a lie and nothing would be all right ever again.

Take a breath, he told himself, after moving the last object out of the way of the garage doors and seeing the car was free. The damned thing probably wouldn't start anyway, and even if it did, it would need to be taxed, MOT'd and insured.

The knowledge that he wouldn't be going anywhere in it anytime soon, hit him hard, and George sank to the floor, coming to a rest on his haunches with his head buried in his hands.

He could almost deal with the fact that everyone knew he had a problem. It no longer mattered what the residents of Applewell thought, and he couldn't work out why it ever had. They meant nothing to him and he meant even less to them – so why had he been so terrified that his tendency to hang onto things in case they came in handy one day would be discovered?

Logically, he knew it didn't make sense that he felt such deep shame. But everyone would be talking about him, saying he couldn't cope, that he was letting things slide, that he needed help.

George lifted his head.

They'd be right – he *did* need help. He needed help in getting away from here, and there was only one person he could think of. Donald Mousel. Buses mightn't run on a Friday evening in Applewell, but Donald's taxi might. If he hadn't downed too many pints in the Busy Bumble, that is.

Taking a chance, George found the man's phone number and gave him a call.

'What, now?' Donald asked when George identified himself and told him where he wanted to go.

'It'll cost you,' Donald warned. 'Aberystwyth and back is a fair few miles.'

'I know how far it is. Don't worry about the money.'

'Why do you want to go there, then?'

'That's hardly any of your business. Will you take me or not?'

'I suppose I'd better. I'll be there in ten minutes. I'm just finishing my tea.'

George ended the call, his mind on what he needed to pack. He didn't particularly want to go to Aberystwyth, but it was the nearest place he could get to that he could catch a train to Liverpool from.

He should never have left the city.

Stuffing a random assortment of clothes and toiletries into his fabric shopping bag, he stared wistfully at his computer. He'd need it eventually, but not for a few days. Once he got to Liverpool, he could sort himself out with somewhere to live, and as soon as he had a roof over his head, he could hire a car and come back for it, and anything else he needed. The only other thing he grabbed before he heard Donald's taxi pull up outside and beep the horn, was a document file and his wallet.

With one last look around the place he'd lived in for so many years, George slipped through the door and out into the evening sunshine.

He didn't glance at Nessa's cottage once.

–

'Can we take a detour before you take me to the station?' George asked, as the taxi reached the outskirts of Aberystwyth.

'You're the one who's paying,' Donald said.

'I want to go to the hospital.'

'Righto.'

Nothing more was said. Apart from that one exchange, the whole journey had been completed in silence, Donald thankfully not making idle and irrelevant conversation for once.

The taxi pulled up outside the hospital doors and George clambered out.

'I won't be long,' he said, leaving Donald to try to find a parking space. It was coming to the end of visiting time, so a space or two should become free shortly. Anyway, George didn't intend being long – he only wanted to pop in quickly to see Mairi. It didn't sit well with him to disappear without at least saying goodbye.

He only just made the end of visiting time, and after a stern talking-to by one of the nurses and his assurance

281

that he'd be quick, he was allowed onto the ward to see Mairi.

When the old lady saw him, her face lit up and he was relieved to see she looked better than she had the last time he'd visited, although he could still see signs in her face of the stroke she'd suffered.

She held a shaky hand out to him. 'George, how lovely! I wasn't expecting to see you today.' She looked beyond him. 'Where's Nessa?'

He took her hand and kissed her on the cheek. 'She's… I'm… on my own today.'

'Why?' Her tone was sharp and despite her frailty her gaze was keen as she scrutinised him.

He hesitated.

'What have you done?' Mairi asked. 'Have you upset her? I know you, George Nightingale – you can be a curmudgeonly bugger when you want to be.'

'It's not like that!' he protested, wishing he'd gone straight to the railway station.

'What is it like then, hmm?'

'She's upset me, not the other way around,' he grumbled.

'Are you going to tell me about it, or are you going to sulk?'

George was about to say Mairi wouldn't understand, simply so he didn't have to share his shameful secret with her, when he realised she probably knew anyway. If most of Applewell knew about his hoarding problem, then Mairi undoubtedly did – and he'd bet his last penny that Nessa had already told her.

Darn it, he should have thought about that before he popped in to see her.

'George…' Mairi's tone brooked no argument.

'Did she tell you about my, um…?'

'Hoarding? No, she didn't.'

George frowned. 'If she didn't tell you, how do you know?' Even as he said it, he knew he was being naive. He and Nessa wouldn't be the only visitors from Applewell Mairi would have received.

'I think I might have worked it out for myself,' Mairi said with a frown of her own. 'I can't remember. It was a long time ago.'

'What do you mean, "a long time ago"? Nessa has only known for a week or so.' Was that all? It seemed far longer. As did their relationship.

'Oh, I knew long before Nessa moved in. I've known for years. We all have. Or rather, I should say we guessed. Is that what has got you all worked up?'

George dropped onto the hard plastic chair at the side of the bed. 'Damn,' was all he could manage.

'It's true – your hoarding is common knowledge. I don't understand what you're fussing about. You always were a fusser. There's no need to get your boxers in a twist. No one cares a hoot.'

They might if they knew how bad it had become, he thought, as two things struck him at once. They probably didn't know the true horror behind his front door, because no one had been inside his house in years, apart from Nessa. But if no one knew about the extent of it, that meant Nessa hadn't told anyone.

He closed his eyes slowly. When he opened them again, it was to find Mairi studying him. 'I think I might have been somewhat hasty,' he said.

'You'd better tell me all about it,' she said.

So he did.

'I think I should go home,' George said to Donald when he got back in the taxi. Donald didn't say anything, he merely grunted, and the return journey was as equally devoid of conversation as the outward one.

With one exception.

Donald received a phone call.

George wasn't listening, and he didn't for one minute think it had been anything to do with him, until the taxi driver pulled up outside Eleri Jones's cafe and told him to get out.

'If you hadn't noticed, I live on Oak Lane,' George said. He didn't want to walk through Applewell to get home – he'd wanted to be dropped off at the same place he'd been picked up.

'This is a far as I go,' Donald said. 'I was told to bring you here.'

George squinted at him. It was nearly fully dark by now, and he was tired and upset, and all he wanted to do was to curl up on his bed and think about the best way to apologise to Nessa. He wasn't sure how she'd take it, because this was the second time he'd more-or-less accused her of the same thing. He wouldn't blame her if she didn't forgive him this time.

Donald walked over to the cafe's door, opened it, and jerked his head. 'They're in there.'

'Who?'

Donald didn't reply.

George had no time for this and he wasn't in the mood for games. He was about to walk away when Eleri came outside, grabbed his arm and yanked him through the door.

'Hang on—!' he began.

'No, you hang on. I heard about what went on today in the pub.' Eleri let go of him and folded her arms, her expression thunderous.

George was dumbstruck. Sid and Tony flanked her, and they looked as cheesed off as Eleri.

'What's all this about?' George demanded.

'The way you treated Nessa. We know all about it.' Eleri shook her head. 'How could you believe she'd betray your confidence like that? And before you say anything, she didn't tell us what happened between the two of you – Mairi did. They have phones in hospitals, you know.'

George opened his mouth and closed it again, without saying anything.

'It was for your own good,' Eleri continued. 'Mairi wanted to make sure you understood that we all guessed you had a problem, and you aren't blaming Nessa for us knowing.'

George swallowed nervously.

'Now, are you going to do the right thing and apologise to her?' Eleri demanded. 'Or are you going to hide in that house of yours and hope it all goes away?'

'If you lot will let me go about my business, I fully intend to seek Nessa's forgiveness.'

'When?' Sid asked. 'Today? Next week? Next year?'

'Don't leave it too late, will you, mate?' Tony piped up.

'I think you'd best speak to her tonight. Get it out of the way,' Eleri suggested, her expression softening. 'Look, George, we only want what's best for you, but sometimes that means tough love.'

'Is that what this is?' he asked wearily.

'We care about you, mate. We've known you for years and seen what's happened. We're only trying to help.' Tony held his hands out, palms up.

It had taken an old woman in hospital to make him see the truth. George understood that the trio standing in front of him *did* care. He'd expected derision and teasing from the village, but they were only interested in how he was going to repair his relationship with Nessa, rather than that he had so much stuff in his house he was practically a prisoner in it.

Eleri walked over to him and enveloped him in a hug, her voice soft in his ear. 'Don't let her slip through your fingers.'

George stiffened, then ever so slowly relaxed into her embrace, feeling the sting of tears behind his eyes.

'I won't,' he vowed when she released him, and with her cry of, 'Go get 'em, tiger!' ringing in his ears, he dashed off to bare his soul to the woman he loved.

Donald, much to George's chagrin, went with him. 'I'll give you a lift,' he stated, and guided George to the taxi. George had the feeling they didn't entirely trust him.

Chapter 43

Nessa

There was no way Nessa could stay in Applewell a moment longer. She had thought her cottage would be her forever home, but how could she face living next door to George now? One minute they'd been lovey-dovey, the next he'd been accusing her of all sorts. She'd given her heart, her body and her soul to him, and for him to think she could have betrayed him like that...

Swiping at her wet cheeks with the back of her hand, she took a shuddering breath. She knew he had problems, but she'd honestly thought he could overcome them – but maybe they were too deep rooted for him to be able to weed out. She knew he would probably never be free of the urge to hoard, but she'd thought they were getting somewhere, that she was helping him – and now this.

No sooner had she stepped through her front door than she'd started cleaning. Her sense of irony was sharp – her method of coping with stress was to clean. How she had ever thought a neat-freak like her could make things work with a hoarder like George? They were polar opposites. There was no way she could stand his mess, and she realised he wouldn't be able to cope with her need to tidy up and put away. They'd come to resent each other, and eventually their love would crumble to dust.

There was another reason she was on her hands and knees, scrubbing the kitchen floor: she intended to put the cottage on the market — tomorrow if she could. It would be impossible to live next door to George going forwards. She didn't think she could stand knowing the man she loved was only a few feet away, hating the sight of her. She wouldn't do that to herself. Or to him. Despite his ready and total belief that she'd betrayed his secret, she still loved him. And if the only way for her to bear her pain was to move house, then that was what she'd do.

There was nothing to stay in Applewell for. Not any more.

Finding somewhere to rent wouldn't be easy with Sylvia in tow, but she'd manage it.

The poor thing knew something was up with her mistress, because she hadn't left Nessa alone for a second since she'd returned from the pub. The cat had rubbed her furry face against Nessa's legs and arms, her head, her back, and all the while making anxious mewing sounds. At this very moment, she was balancing on Nessa's shoulders, having leapt up onto her mistress's back as soon as Nessa had knelt down to clean the tiles in the kitchen.

'It's going to be OK, Sylvia,' Nessa crooned to her, praying it would be.

Floor cleaned, Nessa sat up slowly, giving Sylvia time to jump down. The cat promptly tried to sit in her lap, and Nessa scooped her up and held her tight, sobbing into her soft fur. God, it hurt. The pain was as real and as raw as if she had a shard of glass buried in her heart.

She was still sitting on the floor when there was the sound of an engine in the lane outside, followed shortly by a knock on the door.

Grabbing a tea towel, she wiped her eyes and went to answer it, assuming it might be Alison who was still staying in her mum's house.

It wasn't.

To her shock, it was George. She hadn't expected to see him for a while. Or maybe not at all – he was so good at keeping himself to himself, she remembered bitterly.

He looked terrible, as though he hadn't slept for a week, and she couldn't help comparing him to the man who had shared her bed earlier today. That man had been happy and joyful. But she also couldn't help comparing him to the man who had looked at her with such hurt and disappointment before he'd stormed out of the pub.

She said nothing, waiting for him to speak.

He didn't seem able to; although his mouth worked, nothing came out.

Nessa noticed a taxi on the lane, its engine idling, an elderly gentleman leaning against it with his arms folded and a determined expression on his face. She recognised the man as being Donald who'd spoken to them in the Busy Bumble earlier, and she wondered where George was going. Had he come to say goodbye?

A chirrup from below made her look down, and Nessa saw Sylvia winding around George's legs, purring, and she wished she could be as carefree and oblivious as her cat.

'What do you want?' she asked, anxious to get this over with. If he was leaving, the sooner he went the sooner she could get back to cuddling her cat and crying.

She could hardly believe he was doing this to her, to *them*, but he was, and she'd have to live with it. Her mind was numb and her body cold with dread – the only part of her that she could feel was her heart, which ached so badly she thought it might shatter.

'You didn't tell anyone,' George said, sounding as though the words were being forced out of him.

'No, I didn't.' She held herself in check. 'We've been here before, remember? You were wrong about me then, and you're wrong about me now.' She smiled sadly. 'They already know, the village, I mean.'

'I know.'

Donald then yelled something from the lane that Nessa wasn't able to catch.

'Go away!' George called over his shoulder.

'I can't,' Donald shouted back. 'I've had strict instructions not to leave until you pair of idiots kiss and make up.'

Nessa assumed he knew he was in for a long wait, if that was the case. They were way past the kiss-and-make-up stage. George had made it clear he didn't trust her – how could he, if he immediately jumped to the conclusion that she'd betrayed his confidence?

It was that realisation which hurt as much as anything. She hated that he could think so little of her.

'I've been kidnapped. It was Mairi's fault.' His expression was aggrieved and incredulous.

Nessa was incredulous, too; is that what he'd come here to tell her?

'I went to visit her and she told me I'm a fool,' he continued. 'She said I have to tell you how sorry I am.'

'And are you sorry? Or are you just here because Mairi told you to?'

'Of course I'm sorry! I've never been as sorry about anything in my life.'

Nessa blinked furiously, fresh tears threatening to spill down her cheeks. 'I can't keep going through this, George.'

George stared over her shoulder. 'You won't have to, everyone knows already, they have done for ages, apparently.'

She could feel his humiliation, she could see it in the set of his shoulders and in the unhappiness in his eyes. All at once she realised she was too close, too involved, to view his problem calmly, and she forced herself to take a mental step back. If he had been one of her patients, would she expect him to recover in less than a week from years of being insular and secretive? She wouldn't – so it wasn't fair of her to expect it from George simply because she had fallen in love with him.

It would take time. And time was the one thing she could give him, along with her love. If he'd allow her.

That he was here and was attempting to apologise was a start.

'It doesn't matter,' she said. 'It's nothing to be ashamed of. No one is perfect.' She hesitated. 'I think I owe you an apology, too. I've been so caught up in trying to help you, that I haven't really considered what *you* want. I shouldn't have forced my friendship on you.'

Tears were freely sliding down her face now, but she made no move to wipe them away.

The sight of them must have affected him, because George shook his head and looked down at his feet. When he raised his eyes again, they were brimming and red.

'You don't owe me an apology,' he began, but she shook her head, and he ground to a halt.

'Shall we call it even?' she suggested, her voice hitching.

He nodded, and she took a deep, shuddering breath. It was going to be all right, after all. As long as she didn't expect miracles and she was patient with him, they'd get there.

Giving Donald a thumbs-up, Nessa grabbed George's hand and pulled him inside. He kicked the door shut behind him, and followed her into the living room. When she let go of him and turned to face him, he looked wary, but there was a hint of hope in his eyes.

'I want to give us another go, if you do,' she said. Instinctively she crossed her arms, then realised how defensive she must look and uncrossed them. 'We can work through this together, but you've got to want to. You've also got to promise me you won't retreat into yourself whenever there's a problem or we hit a rough patch – because there will be rough patches, every couple has them.'

Nessa stopped talking and held her breath, fearing his reply. She knew how difficult this was for him and how far outside his comfort zone he must be right now. But she also knew she was right. George had to *want* to help himself.

He cleared his throat, then regarded her solemnly. 'I'll try.'

Realistically, she appreciated his answer was the best she could hope for, but she said, 'You'd better do more than try – Mairi and the rest of Applewell will be on your case if you don't. You've got my support and that of the whole village. You don't have to be on your own, if you don't want to.'

'I don't want to be on my own ever again,' he said, and she understood what he meant.

She wasn't sure whether he was ready to hear her say she loved him, but, as the saying goes, actions speak louder than words, so Nessa reached out to him, took him in her arms and held on so tightly she hoped he believed her when she vowed, 'You never will be.'

Chapter 44

Nessa

'You said you wanted to start with the hall,' Nessa said to George, as she stood in that very room and tried not to touch anything. To be honest, the prospect of clearing just this one space was daunting, and it had taken George a while to psych himself up. But, as she'd promised, they were going at his pace, not hers.

'I was thinking the primary school might be able to use the newspapers. Should we ask, do you think?' he suggested.

'I don't see why not? Why don't you give them a call and I'll start ferrying them out to the car.' She'd pulled her Ford onto George's drive, in anticipation of having to make several visits to the local recycling centre. However, George's suggestion was preferable (for some of the stacks of papers at least), and she knew he'd feel better about getting rid of them if he could be assured they'd be made use of.

She was on her third trip back from the car when George reappeared. 'Sorry I took so long. I spoke to the headmistress – nice woman – and she said she didn't have any use for them at the moment, but she gave me a few pointers. We had a chat about papier mâché and hedgehogs, would you believe.'

Nessa blinked. The connection between the two eluded her.

George laughed, a light-hearted sound, and it lifted her soul. 'She knows a woman who makes wonderful things out of papier mâché, and the local wildlife sanctuary is always looking for bedding materials for the bottom of cages, and newspapers are ideal. Who knew?'

Who indeed?

'I rang the wildlife place and they said they'll be happy to take this lot,' he gestured to the packed car, 'off our hands.' Suddenly, he looked worried. 'Do you think there's enough to go around?'

Nessa gave him a steady look and tried not to sound judgemental (because she really wasn't being), when she said, 'I think you've got enough to keep both of them supplied for months. Let's finish loading up – I'm sure we can squeeze a few more in – and we can get over there now.'

'Righto.'

George appeared to be positively chirpy, but Nessa had the feeling he was putting on a brave face for her benefit. She knew these first few steps were going to be difficult, but she hoped he'd find it easier the more he got rid of, and the more he could see of the inside of his house.

There, all loaded up. Nessa dusted her hands off on her jeans and waited for George to lock his front door. Already it was easier to open it, and they'd only tackled the stack of papers and leaflets immediately behind it. It was going to be a long job to clear the rest of the house and outbuildings though, and she prayed George was up for it.

–

A couple of weeks later, Nessa placed her hands on her hips and scanned the kitchen. It was looking so much better already. The washing machine was empty (why on earth George had been keeping chipped and broken mugs in it was anyone's guess) and the hob and oven were useable. Not that George had done anything more than switch the appliance on to check it wasn't broken; he ate at her house most of the time. He was more or less living in her cottage now. The fact that she didn't like the thought of him sleeping in a room surrounded by clutter was only part of it. The biggest part was that they hated to be away from each other for even a moment. And she flatly refused to spend any more time than she had to in George's bungalow – not until it was completely cleared, and maybe not even then. It would make an amazing family home, but only after a serious refurb. As it was now, it was firmly rooted in the past, and she could almost feel George's father breathing disapprovingly down her neck as she removed his possessions boxful by boxful.

Squinting around, Nessa imagined the room with a new kitchen. She'd have the fridge over there, and the—

'Are you redecorating my house again?' George had sneaked up behind her. He wrapped his arms around her waist and kissed the back of her neck. She leant into him, feeling the solidity of his chest, and breathed in the woody scent of his cologne.

'Guilty as charged. How about if you—?'

'No, I'm not putting a new kitchen in. You didn't.'

'That's because you painted my cupboard doors for me.'

'I can paint these.'

'Have you seen the state of them? They're falling apart.'

'I'm sure I can repair them.' He released her and opened the nearest cupboard door. 'A couple of screws, a new hinge, and they'll be as good as new.'

Nessa doubted that. 'It's… it's… I honestly don't know what to call that colour. Apricot? No, that's too nice a word.'

'I can paint them,' he insisted.

'Aren't they coated in melamine?'

'Possibly. But with the right prep, I'm certain—'

Nessa put a finger to his lips. 'George, my love, I know you hate throwing anything out and you like to reuse what you can, and while I admire and applaud you for it, this kitchen is beyond saving.'

'I beg to differ. Imagine these cupboards painted a nice blue…?'

'You've just found some blue paint in the garage, haven't you?'

George pulled a face and she knew she was right. She also knew how hard the clear-out had been for him and she was impressed by the progress he'd made. It was still a daily uphill battle to persuade him to part with things and she was learning when to step back. This was his journey, not hers. She was there for emotional support only. And because she loved him. She hadn't told him so yet, but she would soon.

Today was the day to tackle a room she knew George was dreading – his parents' bedroom. She guessed he'd want to hang on to nearly everything in it. But he'd also told her his mother's clothes were still in the wardrobe and drawers, and it simply wasn't good for his emotional health to continue to keep everything that belonged to her.

'Shall we get started?' Nessa asked. 'Remember the mantra? Three piles?'

He nodded, but she could see the reluctance on his face.

'You don't have to, if you don't want to,' she reminded him.

'I don't *want* to, but I do *have* to. I've been thinking, you see. About what would happen if I died.'

'Hush, I don't want to hear such talk.' The very thought of something happening to George filled Nessa with cold dread. She'd only just found him – to think she could lose him was unimaginable.

'I'm serious. I've been thinking about this for a while – if I don't make sure all these things go to a good home, they'll be thrown in a skip when I'm gone. I've got no one to leave them to, and even if I did, they'd most certainly bin the whole lot. Mairi suffering a stroke got me thinking about what will happen to her house and all the things she loves. And what will happen to mine.'

'George…'

'It's true. If she has to go and live with her daughter, I bet she won't be able to take everything with her, not even if Alison can sort out a granny-flat. I want to choose what happens to my belongings.'

'That's rather morbid.'

'It's sensible. What means something to me, won't mean anything to anyone else.'

Nessa supposed that was one way of looking at it. 'But you'll still want to keep a few bits and bobs, won't you?' Crikey, was he turning into a minimalist under her very nose?

'Of course. And I know I'll want to keep more than is necessary, too. So that's where you come in. Three piles and the question.'

'OK, then. Are you ready?'

George inhaled deeply and let it out in a whoosh. 'As ready as I'll ever be.'

She took his hand and squeezed it. 'I'm proud of you and I know you can do this. We don't have to do it all today, we can take our time.'

It was going to take more than a day, Nessa knew, but the pair of them set to with determination, Nessa holding things up and asking 'the question': 'If you are going to keep it, what are you going to do with it?'

Keeping it 'just in case' wasn't an acceptable answer. Some things, like the electric drill for instance, were kind of exempt. But a pair of shoes belonging to George's mother wasn't. Once it had been decided they had to go, the other consideration was where should they go to. That was where the three bags came in: one bag for items George intended to keep, one to take to charity, the third for items that were going to be thrown away. Except, Nessa had a problem when it came to the third option. Or rather, *she* didn't, *George* did.

'Surely it could be used for something?' George lamented as Nessa held up an old nightie. It was a brushed cotton one and had seen better days. Faded and bobbled, it wasn't in good enough condition to be given to the charity shop in the village and keeping it wasn't an option either.

'I suppose it could be cut up for dusters,' Nessa suggested doubtfully. 'Ooh, hang on, I've got an idea.' She darted out of the room and out of the front door. She'd left her mobile phone at her own house and there was a number in there she wanted to call.

George was still staring woefully at the nightie when she returned waving her mobile in the air. He narrowed his eyes at her.

'It's a good idea, I promise,' she said, scrolling until she found the number she needed and hit call.

'Gracie? It's Nessa Millbrook, how are you?' She put it on speaker phone so George could listen in.

'Good, thanks. And you?'

'Never better.' Nessa shot George a big grin. 'George is having a bit of a clear-out, and he wondered if you'd have any use for those old clothes that aren't good enough for the charity shop? I don't expect you to take all of them, or even any of them if they're of no use to you, but I thought I'd ask.'

'It's surprising what you can get from old clothes,' Gracie said. 'Buttons, hooks and eyes, zips, ribbons, lining material, and often some parts of the fabric are reusable.'

'Would you like me to drop a couple of bags to you, or would you like to come here and have a rummage through?'

Nessa could see George waving frantically at the suggestion that Gracie came to the bungalow, but she ignored him. He was never going to be a social butterfly, but it would do him good to speak to another person besides her. The only other person he seemed comfortable with was Mairi, who had been moved to another hospital further away, as it provided longer-term care until she had recovered enough to be discharged.

Anyway, Nessa had no intention of letting Gracie step foot inside George's bungalow – she was aware it was a step too far for him right now, but there was nothing wrong with Nessa taking the woman to the cottage. As soon as George had filled some bags, Nessa would put them in her living room for Gracie to have a look through.

She arranged for Gracie to pop over to her house later that afternoon and after the call ended Nessa explained, 'She makes all kinds of things out of scrap material.'

'So no landfill?' he asked.

'There probably will be some,' Nessa observed, 'but that will only be for those things no one can possibly do anything with.'

George sighed. 'OK. Let's put the nightie in a bag for Gracie and hope she can find a use for it.'

—

Nessa dragged one of the bags across to where Gracie was sitting on the sofa and untied it. George was in his own house, working so he said, but Nessa guessed he didn't want to watch Gracie going through his mother's clothes. She also understood that he wasn't quite ready for interacting with anyone else except for her and Mairi. And occasionally Alison, considering she had moved into her mother's house on a temporary basis from Friday to Monday. During the week she was back in her own house in Swansea due to her work commitments. Nessa didn't mind visiting Mairi when Alison wasn't able to, and neither did George. She suspected he quite enjoyed it.

Gracie's face, when she delved inside the bag, was a picture. 'My word, this is wonderful!' she cried, lifting out the first thing she touched. It was an old coat made out of Welsh wool in a traditional pattern. The seam on one of the sleeves was torn, the hem had come loose, and the lining was hanging down. It had also lost two buttons and was looking very sorry for itself.

'I can mend this,' Gracie announced with glee, then dived right back in.

When she brought out the nightie which had started the whole thing off, she told Nessa, 'I can cut it into strips to make hair.'

'Excuse me?'

'Fabric hair for dolls. This type of material, when cut fine enough, tends to roll in on itself into long tubes – perfect for making hair.'

'Okaaay...'

'You'll have to pop around one day and I can show you what I mean.'

The one and only time Nessa had been inside Gracie's house was when she'd picked up her altered curtains and the cushions Gracie had made for her. 'I'll call in next time I'm in the village,' she vowed.

Gracie ended up taking almost everything, and all that was left were a few bits and bobs.

But before she left, Gracie said something that gave Nessa another idea on how to shift some more of George's things. Nessa was sure it would also appeal to George's waste-not-want-not approach, whilst encouraging him to engage with the residents of Applewell at the same time.

All she had to do was to persuade him to go along with it.

Chapter 45

George

George uncurled himself from where he'd been big-spooning Nessa and inched out of bed. It was early, only the birds and Sylvia had beaten him to it, but he was too uptight and nervous to sleep. He'd been awake for ages, mulling things over, worrying about what people would say, and what they'd think.

Most of what he called 'packaging' had been cleared from his bungalow, things such as all the cardboard, the empty tins, the cartons and the paper. But even after taking lots of bags of clothing and other assorted household items to the charity shop (they were a bit overwhelmed, he thought), there was still an inordinate amount of stuff he simply didn't know what to do with.

Nessa, however, did.

He hadn't been too keen on her suggestion at first. He'd point-blank refused, but he eventually relented when he realised that Catrin and the local charity shop wouldn't take everything he had to offer. She certainly wouldn't take the jars of nails and screws in the garage, or the blackened carburettor, or the boxes of broken crockery which he simply hated to throw away. But someone might find a use for them...

So, in a few hours' time (four and a half, to be precise) his front lawn would be swarming with people.

The idea terrified him.

But he was even more scared that no one would turn up at all; what if everyone shunned him – the way he'd been doing to them for years?

Unable to keep still, George slipped some trainers on his feet and returned to the bungalow. He may as well start setting up the tables and laying blankets and sheets on the ground ready to spread whatever he could on them. He'd already decided that if he had two or more of something, he'd keep one – depending on what it was. Things like lengths of wood or pieces of hardboard would remain firmly in the shed because, as had recently been demonstrated by the boarding up of his dining-room window and of Mairi's front door, such miscellaneous items actually did come in handy one day. He had been forced to concede he didn't need three jam jars full of the same sized nails, though.

He was busily laying things out on one of the tables when Nessa appeared, blearily rubbing her eyes.

'You've started without me,' she observed through a yawn.

'Don't worry, there's plenty to go around. Fancy a brew?'

'I'll make it and I'll throw a couple of rashers under the grill while I'm at it. We'll have a bacon sarnie before the hordes arrive.'

'Do you think many people will come?'

'I think loads will turn up, out of curiosity if nothing else.'

304

'Hmm. Can I stay indoors? It's not as if I'm charging for any of this. They don't need my help to cart off whatever they fancy.'

'No, you can't stay inside. That would look odd.'

'Don't care,' he replied. But he did care. Deep down he'd always cared, which was why he'd cut himself off from everyone in the first place; he hadn't wanted them to think badly of him when they realised what his house was like. When they realised what *he* was like.

George nudged Nessa. 'You'd better get a move on with those sarnies. We've got visitors already.'

Sid was hurrying up the pavement and George tried a smile out for size. It didn't fit particularly well, but he kept it there anyway and hoped it would feel more natural as the morning went on. 'Sid, nice to see you.'

'Is it? Oh… Nice to see you, too.' Sid shot Nessa's retreating figure a knowing look. 'We're all chuffed to see you back with Nessa. I hated to think of you rotting out here all on your own.'

Rotting? George would hardly refer to his previous solitary existence as *rotting*.

'You deserve a bit of happiness at your age,' Sid carried on, and George's mouth dropped open. At his age, indeed. Sid was seven years older than him! What a cheek.

Before George could think of a suitable comeback, Sid added, 'It's no fun going through life all on your own. I should know.' He looked quite disconsolate and George felt a wave of sympathy wash over him. He hadn't realised Sid was lonely – the newsagent had always seemed so jovial.

'Never mind, I've got my two sons and the grandchildren, and all my friends, so I shouldn't grumble. But if your Nessa has a friend…?' Sid chuckled.

She *was* his Nessa, wasn't she? The thought warmed George even more than the sun in the brilliant blue sky overhead. It was shaping up to be a wonderful day, in more ways than one.

'I can't stay long,' Sid said, casting his gaze over the plethora of items on the lawn. 'I wanted to pop by and show my support – and see if there's anything I think might come in handy. Actually—' He paused and walked across to a blanket covered in all things plumbing related. 'That tap looks remarkably like the ones in my bathroom. The hot one is fine, but the cold one has got a crack in it. I thought I'd have to replace both of them because they're that old you can't get them any more.' Sid picked up the tap and examined it. The enamel on the top which indicated whether the water was hot or cold was missing. 'I suppose I could use the top bit from my existing one. It looks like it only screws in. Do you mind if I take it?'

'Help yourself, that's what this is all about.'

'And you don't want anything for it?'

George shook his head.

'Cheers, mate. The next time you pop in for a paper it's on the house.' Sid gave him a nod and left.

George didn't want to say so, but the days of him buying a newspaper were long gone. If he had ever read the ones he'd bought then it might be a different story, but each one had remained pristine and unopened. Looking back, he realised how much of a waste that habit had been, but at least the papers had all gone to good causes.

By the time Nessa returned, carrying a tray laden with two mugs of tea and two plates of bacon sandwiches, more people had arrived. He recognised Lottie Hargreaves, who'd managed to escape without her three children, Eleri Jones, who smirked and winked at him, and Catrin

Williams, who managed the charity shop. Over the course of the morning it seemed that most of Applewell appeared to have trotted up his drive. Even Donald Mousel and Mrs Hayworth put in an appearance, and George recalled that his awkward conversation with Mrs Hayworth in Sid's shop had been when he had first heard Nessa's name. If he'd have known then what he knew now, he'd have given Mrs Hayworth a great big hug.

Most people took at least one item away with them, and some of them took several. And all the while, George could hear them saying things like, 'I've been looking for one of those', or 'that's just what I wanted'. He knew he'd have stuff left over and he was prepared for that (kind of), but what he wasn't prepared for was the volume of support he received. Many people told him how pleased they were to see him (he heard the unspoken undercurrent that they'd hardly seen much of him at all over the years), and they all seemed genuinely delighted he and Nessa were a couple. Even if he wanted to hide his feelings for her, he couldn't, especially when she kept slipping an arm around him or giving him a kiss on the cheek.

One of the last people to show up was Alison.

'How's Mairi?' Nessa asked, as she did every time she saw her.

Alison heaved a sigh. 'Grumpy, fed-up, a terrible patient… but apart from that, she's doing well. They're on about letting her out soon.'

'That's fantastic news.' George saw Alison's expression. 'Isn't it?'

'Not really. She wants to come back here to live. I've told her it's impossible. She won't be able to cope on her own for ages, if at all; she'll have to move in with me. She isn't happy, and to be honest – I know it's a dreadful thing to say – but neither am I. She'll hate living with me, and if she's miserable, I will be, too. But I can't have her living so far away because she'll need checking on a couple of times a day, even if she does manage to go back to her own house.'

'Have you thought about a granny-flat?'

'My husband and I have talked about it and we've had a look at what's out there, but we haven't seen anything suitable within our price range. Not unless Mum sells the cottage and we put the money towards it, which she's refusing to do.'

'It's not easy, is it?' Nessa said, sympathetically, and George knew what she meant. His father, although knowing he needed care, hadn't been too happy when George had had to move back in. George himself hadn't been too pleased either, for that matter. His father had needed help, and George had given it willingly and with love, but that didn't mean either of them had found their new living arrangements to their liking.

'If there's anything we can do…?' Nessa continued.

Alison smiled sadly. 'That's very kind of you, you've been wonderful neighbours. Once I've got Mum living with me, if you could keep an eye on her house until we know what's going to happen to it, that would help enormously. I don't want to have to keep driving up to check on it.'

'Of course we will. Let us know when you have a date for her discharge. We'd like to say goodbye if she does end up moving to Swansea with you,' Nessa said.

George hoped the goodbye was only temporary and that Mairi would return to her cottage to live one day. Now that he'd come to know his neighbour better he didn't want to lose her, and if she could live there on her own, he vowed he'd do everything he could to help.

Help and kindness were the things that made the world a better place, and since Nessa had moved in next door, he'd had both in abundance.

There was also something else that made the world a better place, and that was love.

He couldn't believe how lucky he was to have found it.

George waited until Alison, and the few stragglers who were still lingering amongst the depleted items strewn across his lawn, left.

It was time – he had to tell Nessa how he felt about her.

He should take her out for a romantic meal and tell her then. But telling her here, surrounded by the remnants of his old life, seemed more fitting. What remained on his lawn was the last of it. Once it was bagged up and removed, there would be nothing left – just a new life and a new beginning. He hoped to share that new life with Nessa, the woman who had made it all possible. The woman he didn't want to live without.

'Nessa?' He heard the hesitancy in his voice, and he knew his insecurities would probably never go away entirely – some scars were too deep, the hurt embedded too far – but with Nessa beside him...

'Hmm?' She looked up from gathering up the few remaining items on one of the tables.

Now he had her attention, he wasn't sure how to proceed. Should he start by thanking her? Oh, what the hell – he should just say it. 'I love you.'

'I know. I love you, too.'

'Do you?'

'Of course I do!'

'You've never said.'

'I was waiting for you to realise you loved me. I didn't want to scare you off.'

How well she knew him, he thought. He might have fallen in love with her as early as when she was walking Sylvia around the garden on a lead, but if he had, he hadn't known it. He wasn't sure when he'd fallen in love; it had been a gradual thing, creeping up on him as stealthily as a cat crept up on a bird in the garden. One day he had just known.

'Would you… do you think you'd… I mean…' he stammered. Goodness, why was this so hard? 'Move in with me?' he finally blurted.

Nessa barked out a laugh and his heart dropped to his boots. 'Not a chance. Not until you've done something with that awful kitchen. And possibly not even then. I've got a better idea – *you* move in with *me*. You're practically living at mine already. And once you've tarted the bungalow up, you can put it on the market.'

George stared at her. 'You think I should sell it?'

'I do. You're not happy there.'

She was right. It was time to move on, and the best way to do that was to sell the bungalow. It would be weird living next door to it and seeing someone else in the house that had once been his. But he could cope with it.

With Nessa at his side, he could cope with anything.

She wouldn't give him any other choice.

310

Epilogue

George

George felt there should be a ceremony of some kind to mark the occasion of his last day of owning the bungalow.

He'd sold it and he hadn't even had to put it in the hands of an estate agent to deal with. It belonged to Mairi now. After a considerable amount of argy-bargy between her and Alison, the pair of them had agreed to sell Mairi's cottage and for Mairi to move into the bungalow instead. Single-storey living would suit Mairi better, and with some modifications and a great deal of redecoration (which George and Nessa had promised to help with), it would make the perfect home for her. It would also mean she wouldn't have to move away from the village she loved so dearly, because he and Nessa were on hand to keep an eye on her. Alison had taken quite a lot of persuading, but in the end she'd acquiesced.

George took a final look around. Devoid of all the clutter and most of the furniture, it no longer felt like the house he'd lived in for a substantial part of his life. Yet, when he closed his eyes, he could still feel the lingering presence of his parents and the ghost of the person he used to be. It was good he didn't have to completely sever all ties with it. It was also good that the house wouldn't have a stranger living in it. Mairi, he knew, would take care of it.

He should go back to the cottage. Nessa was due home from the wildlife sanctuary soon, where she helped out three days a week taking care of injured animals. He loved hearing her stories about the little creatures she'd helped nurse back to health, and he held her while she sobbed over the ones who didn't make it, tears also trickling down his own cheeks.

These last five months had certainly been a roller coaster of emotions and George suspected life with Nessa would always be full of love and laughter, tears and kindness. She had brought vibrancy and light into his world, and had forced him out of the gloom he'd previously been living in. He now felt as though he lived life in the sun. Metaphorically, at least, because sunshine could never be guaranteed in Wales and it had been raining on and off for the past two weeks.

It had eased off today, and George had popped around to the bungalow to check on the garden and make sure the lawn didn't need cutting again. He was determined to help Mairi as much as possible with its upkeep, and a garden this size needed to be controlled else it would quickly run wild. Mairi loved her garden, and although she wouldn't be able to do much more than potter in it, he would be there to do the heavy stuff so she could enjoy sitting outside.

This wouldn't be the last time he would set foot inside the bungalow's walls, but today he felt as though he was saying goodbye. Later he was due to hand the keys to Alison for her to begin renovations. George took a minute to compose himself in the hall before he opened the front door, stepped through it and walked away from his old life for good.

A sudden movement at his feet and the brush of a sleek sinuous body against his legs made him jump.

'Sylvia!' he cried, looking down to see the cat winding around his ankles. She rubbed her face against his knees and purred. The sound was vaguely reminiscent of a pneumatic drill.

He frowned; there was something else on the doorstep besides the cat, and he bent down to take a closer look.

What on earth was a cake tin doing there, and, more importantly, why did it have a piece of paper on top of it with a small stone holding it in place?

He glanced across to the cottage. Nessa's car was already there; he'd been so wrapped up in his memories he hadn't heard her return.

However, she was nowhere in sight, so he picked up the cake tin. Taking the pebble and the piece of paper from the top of it, he wedged the tin under one arm and read the note.

> *Just a little something from me to you to say,*
> *'I love you'.*
>
> *Your wife,*
> *Nessa x*
> *(Nessa Nightingale)*

What the—? They weren't married...

A slow smile spread across his face and he carefully folded the note, putting it in his pocket. This was one piece of paper he had every intention of keeping, and he didn't think Miss Neat Freak next door would object on this occasion.

Was she asking what he hoped she was asking?

He slipped the pebble in his pocket too – that was something else he intended to hang on to – and turned his attention to the tin. It was the same one in which she'd put the very first cake she'd made him.

With his heart in his mouth, he eased the lid open.

Inside was one solitary cupcake.

The familiar aroma of sugar and vanilla wafted up his nose and he inhaled deeply. The cake had a swirl of mint-green butter icing on the top, the same shade as Nessa's kitchen cupboard doors. But that wasn't what captured George's attention.

A flat white disc made of icing sugar sat on top of the buttercream. It had two scrolls painted on it and writing in between.

Will you marry me?

He didn't know what to say. Or rather he did, but he was so overwhelmed he didn't think he could get the word out.

George took the cake out of the tin and popped it on the hall table – his mouth was too dry to take a bite and he didn't think the butterflies in his stomach would allow him to eat it, so he'd come back for it later.

He had more important things to do right now than eat cake.

He had an answer to give.

Nessa felt sick. What if he said no? It didn't bear thinking about, yet the thought kept circling through her mind, making her giddy with fear.

How would she move on from such a rejection? How could *they* move past it as a couple?

Oh, God, why did she have to ask?

They were fine as they were. There had been no need for her to rock the boat, no need for them to be married. They loved each other regardless of a ring and an official piece of paper.

But she was traditional that way.

She wanted to marry him, damn it. She wanted to be his wife. She wanted to belong to him and for him to belong to her, and if that went against the current trend to live together and have partners instead of spouses, she didn't care.

But what if he said no? How would he tell her?

She should have asked him face to face, not written a silly note and made an even sillier plaque for the top of an equally silly cake.

What had she done?

Nausea roiled in her stomach and she swallowed, her mouth dry. Her heart was tippy-tapping so hard she thought she might faint. Surely he'd read the note and seen the cake by now? What was he doing in the bungalow anyway? He'd been in there for what seemed like hours.

Nessa checked her watch. Ten minutes, that was the amount of time that had elapsed since she'd crept up the bungalow's drive and left the tin.

It felt like a lifetime.

A noise outside startled her even though she'd been waiting for it, and she rubbed her damp palms on her jeans and tried not to throw up.

A faint meow then told her it wasn't George outside her front door.

Nessa let out a slow breath.

Sylvia could have picked a better time, and she also could have come around the back and used the cat flap George had installed for her.

Another meow.

With a sigh, Nessa went to the door and opened it with trembling fingers. Sylvia shot inside with a chirrup. Nessa ignored her, and quickly peeped at the bungalow's front step before she closed the door.

The cake tin was gone.

Something on her own step caught her eye and she glanced down. Her tin was sitting there, a small piece of paper on top held in place by a familiar pebble.

Hardly daring to breathe and with her heart hammering so fast she thought she might pass out, Nessa reached for it. She could tell by the weight of the tin that it was empty.

Gingerly, she opened the note. George had written his reply directly underneath hers.

Yes, please.

George Nightingale

Nessa slumped shakily against the wall.

He'd said yes. Yes! Yes, yes, *yes*!

She didn't hear George come in through the kitchen door, but when she felt his arms slip around her waist and felt his lips on her hair, she sank back into him. This was where she belonged, where she was meant to be, and when she twisted around to face him, she saw the joy in her face reflected in his.

'I should call you Florence,' he murmured. 'I've got my very own Nurse Nightingale. Nessa Nightingale. It has a certain ring to it, don't you agree?'

She did agree, and to show him how much she agreed, she kicked the door shut with her foot, took his hand and led him upstairs. They had a couple of hours before Alison was picking up the keys and Nessa didn't want to waste it.

Waste not, want not, as George often said…